FIRE-FIGHTIN' MOSE

FIRE-FIGHTIN' MOSE;

BEING:

An Account of the Life and Times
of the

World's Greatest Fire Fighter,

Member of the
New York City Volunteer Fire Department,
and of the Company of

Lady Washington,

Engine No. 40,
a machine of greatest excellence,
known as the

WHITE GHOST.

By

HAROLD W. FELTON,

Illustrated by Aldren A. Watson.
Foreword by B. A. Botkin.

NEW YORK: ALFRED A. KNOPF, 1955.

LIBRARY OF CONGRESS CATALOG CARD NUMBER: 55–6100

© HAROLD W. FELTON, 1955

THIS IS A BORZOI BOOK,
PUBLISHED BY ALFRED A. KNOPF, INC.

To Abe

Foreword

ONCE *in a blue moon a natural man comes along and finds himself perfectly cast as a natural hero. Like every red-blooded American boy, young Mose wanted to be a fireman when he grew up. He was luckier than most boys, who never get to be more than "fire buffs" or fans. For he lived in the days of the volunteer fire department, when engines were drawn and pumped by hand. Those were the days of wooden buildings and iron men, when a man had to be mightier than the machine to make up for its deficiencies, and there was much more opportunity for romantic adventure and gallant heroism.*

Big Mose was our first folk hero of the city. He is here portrayed against an authentic background of Little Old New York of the 1830's. Like a typical

Horatio Alger hero, Mose worked his way up from the bottom. He began by fixing bunks in the firehouse, polishing brass, and carrying a torch during night alarms. Then, a printer by trade, he took his place at the ropes and "ran with the machine." A Bowery boy, he spoke Bowery slang, dressed in Bowery style, had a Bowery girl, Liza, for a sweetheart, and fought rival companies and gangs with the same zest as fires. Because he had all the makings of a hero of melodrama, Mose the Bowery Boy soon became a popular figure on the stage, which put the finishing touches on him as a diamond in the rough and protector of women and children, who saw his duty and did it.

Mose had the necessary trappings as well as attributes of the city hero. In street brawls he used a butcher's cleaver for a knife and plucked cobblestones from the street for ammunition. For amusement he blew sailing vessels out to sea when they tried to make port. Mose was a card!

No hero ever loved his job more fiercely than Mose or felt his responsibility more keenly. In those days it was a point of honor to be the first at a fire and at the nearest hydrant and to be allowed to "take the butt" or hold the end of the leather hose. It was also a matter of pride to keep one's engine as trim and lovely as any ship or horse. In place of the warrior's steed and sword, Mose had his beautiful, beloved LADY WASHINGTON—*the White Ghost*—*and a pair of wonderful Indian rubber boots. When he wanted to jump from the window of a blazing building he tossed his boots into the street below and leaped gracefully and safely into them.*

If those boots were born in the imagination of Harold Felton, in this first full-scale portrayal of the Bowery giant and patron saint, they are quite in character and tradition. Didn't Slue Foot Sue, the wife of Pecos Bill, have a bustle made of spring steel wire and whalebone that kept her bouncing when she was thrown by Bill's horse, Widow Maker? Mose is essentially a tall-tale hero; and as the chronicler of Paul Bunyan, Pecos Bill, and John Henry, Harold Felton is an old hand at making the truth sound like a lie and a lie sound like the truth. In the words of Big Mose, whose flaming red hair and red shirt will blaze forever as a beacon of strength and courage, his biographer may say modestly: "Shucks! It ain't nothin'. I only done me dooty!"

B. A. BOTKIN

Contents

FIRE-FIGHTIN' MOSE

Young Mose

(IN WHICH *a wild fire flames in the night; Mose, a boy in Little Old New York; a burning ambition; a giant, flaming torch and a city in danger; Mose has a plan; a sailor intervenes; "A man's got a right to be scared in a place of danger"; "You can't win all the time."*

BONG! Bong! Bong! The fire bells threw their thrilling call out over the city.

One by one, soft yellow lights appeared behind a hundred frosty windows. An evil glow of fire lit up the sky. Silhouettes of buildings, black and silent, stood out before the red light behind them.

3

Fire! Not a tame fire happily imprisoned at the tip of a candle, dancing lightly at the end of a wick. A slender bit of cotton embedded in a tallow candle. Not a friendly fire flickering gaily or slumbering gently on a hearth. But a wild fire! An enemy, burning with hate, eager to devour. A wild fire, raging with uncontrolled anger. Feeding on everything that would burn. Destroying everything that would not burn. Grasping, reaching out with hot claws. Struggling to reduce the city to ashes. Fighting to take the lives and the homes of the good people on the banks of the Hudson.

A tame fire brings cheer, but a wild fire brings terror!

Fire! The fearful word spread from the metal tongues of bells to the lusty tongues of men, to the shrill tongues of women, and to the trembling, whispering tongues of children. Children who were firmly told to stay in their warm beds and go to sleep.

But who could sleep? What boy could sleep when the noise of slamming doors and the terrifying word *Fire!* filled the air?

What boy could stay in a warm bed when by kneeling on a cold floor and by pressing his nose

4

tight against the icy glass window, he could see the fire and feel the heat of his own blood racing through his veins?

Not Mose. No. Not Mose who was born among the tall buildings of the big city. Three, four, even five stories, the buildings were. And they stood closely packed, row on row. Endlessly they stood, from the Battery, where the ocean water washed the tip of Manhattan's toe, to Chambers Street. Beyond Chambers Street even, along the edges of Broadway and Bowery Lane.

His knees pressed against the cold floor and his nose flattened out on the still colder window pane and he knew he must go to that fire, and to all fires to come. He must go. He must!

But his mother knew better. "Mose!" she said firmly, as she came into the room: "Go right straight back to bed and go to sleep!"

Mose went back to bed. But he did not go to sleep. He could see the wild light against the frosty window. And it made the white frost shine pink.

Why should a boy be in bed at such a time? Why was it worse to be at the window, trembling with cold, than it was to be in a warm bed, trembling with excitement?

5

The light of day came slowly. And when it was no more than a hope over the hills of distant Brooklyn, Mose was out of bed, and dressed, and in the kitchen. He ate his breakfast as his mother said he should. Then he was in the street and the world of smoke and flame was his.

He saw it all. The lumber yard was on fire, in the shadow of St. Paul's Church, on Broadway. Sparks flew up with the wind. The church steeple towered above the flame. But smoke and sparks swirled around it.

He saw it all. The engines and the men pumping at the brakes. The half-inch streams of water spitting at the fire in the lumber yard.

He saw it all. The leather water buckets passed from hand to hand from the well on Broadway to the little fire engines. Water dumped into the engines' boxes. Pumped by men at the brakes through the pipe in a brave half-inch stream that flew against the flaming enemy.

When fire came to Little Old New York Town the entire city was in danger. Fear of fire was always there. The people remembered the fire that almost destroyed the city when General Washington re-

6

treated before the British in 1776. The war had passed by and left the city almost whole. But the fire did not pass by. It caught, and held, and burned.

The people remembered the many fires before that time and since. And they were filled with fear.

Yes. Mose saw it all. He saw what the others did not see.

"Look!" he cried. His boy's voice sounded above the roar of flames, the thump of the pumping brakes and the shouts of men. His finger pointed up to the towering church steeple.

A spark had struck the spire. A dying fire was born again. A thread of smoke, a wisp of flame. In a few moments the towering steeple would turn into a torch, looming far above the roof tops. The small red glow would soon burst into a flaming flower of destruction, hurling burning embers far out over the city below.

Here was the seed of calamity. Here was the threat of a thousand homes in flames.

There was no time to spare. There was no light of hope in the eyes that looked upward. No water could fly that high. Not even from the biggest fire engine. No ladder could reach. There seemed to be no hope.

7

But, as Mose had first looked up, now he looked down. He pushed through the crowd and ran up to the church. He grasped the lightning-rod cable and started to pull himself up.

Of the hundreds watching, one responded. A sailor he was, by the cut of his clothes. He took up a coil of rope and put it under his belt. He reached up for Mose and brought him down to earth.

"It's a good eye you have, son," he said. "And it's a good heart you have too. But I'm a-thinkin' you're much too young to have an arm that's strong enough for this work. You won't be mindin' it if I do what only you seen could be done."

Mose did mind. But the sailor was right. The muscles of his arms bulged as he went up the cable hand over hand.

At the belfry he ran the rope through his belt and dropped the ends to the ground. "Tie a bucket of water to one end, mates," he shouted.

He turned and faced the steeple. Up he went. Up the sheer, dry, shingle steeple to the growing flame. Once there, hanging like a fly, he turned his head and shouted down again: "Water! Pull away!"

The ropes tightened. The dead weight of the

leather bucket pulled down as the men below pulled the rope through his belt. A leather pulley, it was. And up the water went. Past the window. Past the belfry. And up to the man clinging to the cable.

A tug of war, it was. The men on the ground and the heavy bucket pulling down. And the man in the air seeming to hang on the edge of space while the rough rope creaked grudgingly over his tough leather belt. But maybe he was hanging on a hinge of the gates of heaven, for luck was with him, and his strength held, and the bucket of water reached him.

A little water will put out a little fire. And the water from the leather bucket quenched the small flame before it grew into a torch big enough to destroy a city.

The sailor returned to the ground. The larger fire there still burned. The earthbound turned to it. The sailor melted into the crowd and walked down the steep hill toward the Hudson. Mose followed him.

He approached the slip where the bark *Ocean Pearl* was tied. Mose drew near. The sailor saw him and smiled. "You was the only one that seen how to do it," he said. "Too bad you wasn't quite big enough to turn the trick yourself."

11

"I just wanted to thank you," said Mose.

"Why, thanks to you instead. You're the only one who thought of that, too."

Mose's eye fell on the ship. The masts and ropes pointed to the sky like skeletons of church steeples.

"That's the *Ocean Pearl*. That's my ship," the sailor said. "You wantin' to go to sea?"

"No, sir," said Mose.

"Sure, most small lads the size of you want to go to sea, I was always thinkin'," said the sailor.

"Not me," said Mose.

"What then?" the sailor asked.

"When I grow up," Mose replied, "I want to be a fireman."

"But that ain't no trade. You don't get paid for that. That's done by volunteers. They don't get paid, I've heard. An' most often, they don't even get no thanks."

"I'll have some other work, like all firemen do. But it's a fireman I want to be," Mose insisted.

"More power to you, then. But you're not alone in wantin' to be a fireman. Lots of lads do, I've been told."

"Was it hard? Climbin' up? and hangin' on like that?" Mose asked.

"Yes, an' no. I'm used to climbin' ropes an' such."

"Was yez scairt?" Mose blurted out.

"Listen to you now. Was I scared? Yes, I was scared. A man's got a right to be scared in a place of danger. But it's all sort of a game. And you can't win all the time. I got some busted bones to prove it. No, sir. You can't win all the time."

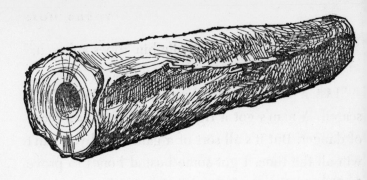

The "White Ghost"

(IN WHICH *is set forth the names of some famous fire engines and tales concerning them;* Lady Washington Engine No. 40, *and Mose's affection for her; a boy's work at the engine house; the* White Ghost; *a way to dress and get downstairs with efficiency and dispatch; Mose becomes a volunteer fireman.*

THE town on the banks of the Hudson grew. It was a pleasant place. A town of gentle hills, with pretty brooks and peaceful ponds, backed by gardens, orchards, and farms to the north.

North of town, Broadway became Bloomingdale Road and led away toward Manhattanville, halfway

14

up Manhattan Island. Then it wound over the hills and dipped into the valleys and crossed the brooks, aiming toward the Hudson River towns.

The Bowery Lane farther east pointed north past the old Stuyvesant farm or bouwerie that gave the road its name. It crossed the little creek, called Crommessie Vly by the Dutch, and Gramercy, by the English, who had their troubles pronouncing Dutch words. It skirted Murray Hill, passed the little villages of Yorkville and Harlem, and courageously set out for New England and Boston.

Mose grew. And he was a part of the city. A boy, but still a part of the city.

The Volunteer Fire Department grew too. Not as much as the city. Not as fast. But it grew, a little. And Mose watched it grow. He knew all the fire engines. He knew the old ones and the new ones. He knew their numbers. The numbers they gave them at City Hall, to tell one engine from another in the official records. But the numbers were cold.

He knew the names of the fire engines, too. Names given to the engines by the people. Names that came from the hearts of the people. They were friendly names. Warm names. Warm names for fire engines.

Mose knew the numbers and the names. The

15

names were better than numbers. They were good names. Given out of the love of the people.

There was old Number 3. She was the first engine to have a name. *Old Brass Back,* they called her. That was because of the free use of brass that bound and trimmed her box. She was American made. The first American-made fire engine. She was straight and strong. And there were *American, Honey Bee, Protection,* and *Neptune.*

Mose knew the tales of how the engines got their names. He knew of the great Coffee House Slip fire in the winter of 1796 when the city faced destruction. It started on Murray Wharf at the end of Wall Street. Union Engine No. 18 was in the thick of it, taking water from the East River. The fire closed in. The men of Union Engine No. 18 were forced to seek safety in the river. They could not leave their old friend behind to be destroyed by fire. Never! So they took the engine with them into the river for safety.

When she came out, her name was *Shad Belly.* And it was a name of respect, of love. It was a name honored. A name earned.

There was the *Phoenix.* That was a name for a fire engine. It told its own story, for everyone knew that the phoenix was a giant bird that was burned and destroyed, but sprang once more to life from its own ashes.

There was *Hope*. And *Bunker Hill*. And *Columbus*. There was *Bombazula*, later known as the *Black Joke*. There were *Oceanus*, *Ætna*, and *Bean Soup*.

There was *Wreath of Roses*, also known as the *Old Maid*, one of the biggest and most powerful engines.

The head of a tiger was painted on *Big Six*, and that was the tiger that became the symbol of Tammany Hall.

Columbia Hose No. 9 was beautifully decorated with silver plate. They called her *Silver Nine*. Because she was manned by socially prominent men, she was called the Silk Stocking Hose Company.

Aaron Burr for years failed in his efforts to start a bank. He turned his attention to the problem of water. An ample supply for the rapidly growing city was needed. He and other leading citizens formed the "Manhattan Company," which was promptly chartered by the Legislature. Burr wrote the charter, and the charter had a clause, a clause which permitted the Company to use its capital not required in the water business in any moneyed transactions. It was not long before the Company was engaged in the banking business. It also gave the city its first adequate supply of good water, from wells at Centre and Reade Streets, near the Collect Pond. There was a reservoir on Chambers Street, near Broadway. The pumps were operated by horse power, and within a year the Company put down six miles of pipe, made of hollow yellow- or white-pine logs.

That was the water supply, until 1842, when water was piped all the way from the Croton River in the Bronx to a giant reservoir at Forty-Second Street and Fifth Avenue.

Always there were fires in those years of Mose's boyhood. He ran to the fires. He watched them from his bedroom window at night when he could not go. Once, he discovered a fire and ran to the fire bell. And when he pulled the rope and heard the bell, he knew that he had done something good for his city. That day he was a hero.

He loved all fire engines equally. Then one day Mose's life was changed. Something new came into his life. When he saw it, his heart paused. And then it went out. Went out to a fire engine.

Brand, spanking new it was. It was small. It was white. Pure white, and it was trimmed with gold. And on its surface, on its clean, pure-white surface, printed in shining gold, was its name: *Lady Washington, Engine No. 40.*

Beautiful, it was. To Mose, it was the most wonderful and beautiful thing in the world.

Into one small corner of his heart, the lower right-hand corner, he placed all other fire engines. Even the big ones. Even the red ones. And into the remaining big, open space went *Lady Washington, Engine No. 40.* Small, white and gold.

That was in 1812, and the people were thinking and talking about the war. All, that is, except Mose. He was thinking and talking about *Lady Washington, Engine No. 40.* Nothing else. Nothing at all.

He was big now. Well, kind of big. Still, a boy. But a boy who knew what he wanted. He wanted to fight fires and run with *Lady Washington, Engine No. 40.* He was too young for that. But he could help. And he did help.

The fire house in Mulberry Street, near Broome Street, was his second home. Busy Centre Market at the corner of Broome and Centre Streets was little more than a block away. The Bowery, three short blocks east, was an important street in that part of town, even though it did become a country lane a few miles or so farther north.

19

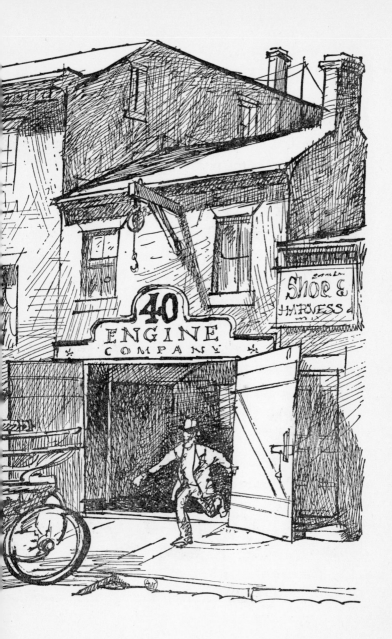

The Bowery had been an Indian trail away back in early Dutch times. Then it became the lane that lead past Buttermilk and Sweetmilk Ponds, to Peter Stuyvesant's farm or bouwerie, far to the north, where Tenth Street and Third Avenue would one day be. It was the post road to Boston, and the city grew with the traffic on such arteries of trade and commerce.

Mose became a voluntary aid as soon as he was old enough. But he was not a fireman. No. Not yet a fireman. He helped wash the engine and dry the leather hose. He swept the floor. He polished the brass and he rubbed the white and gold of the engine until it shone like the setting sun shining across the Hudson. Sore muscles. Bruised knuckles. Blisters. No job in the fire house was too menial or too hard for Mose.

When he was not in school he was at the fire house. When the fire bells rang out, Mose was the first to reach the engine. He took the blocks from under the wheels and stretched the ropes out straight. When the men came running, there was no delay. *Lady Washington, Engine No. 40* was always ready.

She was always first at the fire. Well, nearly always. And as she streaked through the streets by night it reminded Mose of a brave, strong spirit, rushing to conquer the evil red demon, fire.

And the words came to him, and he said: "That enjine slips along, floatin' through the streets like a—a— white ghost."

People heard him and they knew he was right. *Lady Washington, Engine No. 40* was called the *White Ghost* by everyone.

With the *White Ghost,* Mose was on his way to become Mighty Mose, the fireman. But it didn't happen all at once. Often he slept under the engine so he could be there first when the fire bells rang. Then they fixed bunks upstairs. Those who didn't want to miss a fire could sleep there. They called them "bunkers." And Mose was the first bunker.

Before he knew it, he was carrying the torch through the dark streets to light the way for the *White Ghost.* That was a boy's job. The third of the many slow steps toward becoming a volunteer fireman. The second step, as everyone should know, is to polish brass. And the first step, the very first, is to have the heart for fire fighting.

One evening the fire bells rang. The men on the street, members of Engine Company No. 40, turned toward the fire house. They hurried from their homes

23

near by. Mose was then a bunker. He was upstairs in the fire house, in bed.

"Maybe this is one time we'll git to the enjine before Mose does," said the foreman.

He and the others started across the street toward the door. An upstairs window opened. Mose sprang to the window sill and slipped his red suspenders over his shoulder. The brass eagles on the sturdy galluses flashed. His boots were in his hand.

The cry "don't jump!" froze on the foreman's lips and the firemen froze in their tracks.

Mose stood on the window sill in his stocking feet. His hand swung out in an easy, graceful motion. His boots began to fall. It all seemed so casual, so simple. Yet every move was definite and precise.

The boots fell. They were no sooner free from his hand when Mose jumped after them. The boots hit the ground and Mose hit the boots with both feet. It was over! That quick!

The foreman held his breath. The men behind him stood still, like chimneys on the roof tops, never moving a bit. The fire bells were ringing their command, but no one moved.

"I've heard of men being so scared they jumped out of their boots," the foreman whispered with a husky voice. He gulped. "But I never thought I'd live to see a man jump into his boots from a second-story window!"

"Or anywheres else," someone behind him added.

"Yes. Or anywheres else."

But it was so. And they had seen it. In one jump, his boots were on and he was ready to go.

He opened the doors and laid the ropes out before the men crossed the street. Then he turned for his torch, for now it was almost dark, and light would be needed.

"Let the torch go, Mose," said the foreman.

"Don't sack the lad fer jumpin' out the winder," one of the men said.

"I ain't a-goin' ter sack him," the foreman replied. "I'm promotin' him. Right now!"

Mose paused. "To the masheen!" the foreman shouted. He turned to Mose.

"Mose. Lend a hand at the ropes," he said. "You are now a fireman!"

Mose rushed to the pull rope and proudly took it in his hand. The tongue was raised. This was a man's work. He was face to face with the future. The future he had waited and worked for. Now, when he was first at the engine when the fire bells rang, he could work the pipe. He could play the water on the fire. He could—

But there was no time to think. The fire bells were calling. Another boy went ahead with the torch. The men bent against the ropes, and Mose was with them. The *White Ghost* rolled out into the street. The men shouted. She rumbled over the cobblestones toward the Bowery and the red glow of fire.

Mose was a volunteer fireman!

The Gallus Fireman

(IN WHICH *reference is made to some interesting points of New York history; Mose is described in meticulous detail, his figure, face, hair, and raiment; a brief record of fire fighting on Manhattan Island; the Newsham engines;* brandt meisters; *the Revolutionary War and the great fire of 1776; Nathan Hale.*

THERE were many fires in those days. Fire was Public Enemy Number One. It had been so since the beginning. No home, no place of business— nothing was safe from fire. It is so now.

It was fire that first put white men on the shore

27

of Manhattan. Men from the *Tiger*, a ship that was owned by Captain Adrian Block, a Dutchman. She was burned to the water line in 1613. That was before the Dutch traders came. It was long before the Dutch settlers came, and it was thirteen years before Peter Minuit traded twenty-four dollars' worth of beads for Manhattan Island.

It was fire that forced the first Dutchmen ashore. And ever since, fire has been the city's greatest enemy. And several times the enemy almost won. And always the enemy fights.

Little Old New York grew fast from the beginning. In the days of Mose it was still growing. Like a mushroom, as they say. A giant mushroom. It was growing in the only way a city at the southern tip of an island could grow. It was spreading north, and up. Some of the buildings were five stories tall, and some men were thinking about building even taller ones. It almost took a person's breath away to think of it.

New buildings were put up. New streets were made. Made so fast that sometimes policemen had trouble finding their way home. And even the hansom-cab drivers got lost in the multitude of new streets. The volunteer firemen took their engines out and ran through the streets on Sunday afternoons so they would know the best and quickest way to get to fires.

It became as hard to think of new names for streets as it was to remember those already named. In a moment of sensible desperation the streets were given numbers instead of names. Anyone who could count could find his way about.

There were reasons for the square blocks and the big, wide streets that ran straight. It was all part of a plan. The fresh air could go down such wide streets. The clean, fresh winds from the rivers and the clear, refreshing sea breezes would be of great benefit to the people. Moreover, the wide streets would keep fires from spreading, and the firemen could get to fires more easily and quickly.

New York was a clean city. There was very little garbage in the streets, and the reason was simple. Pigs roamed the streets, and they cleaned up the edible refuse that might otherwise have been noisome and unsanitary.

New York was a big and busy town. Full of bustle and business. Street cries filled the air as those with goods or services advertised their wares.

Chimney-sweeps did a thriving business, for the

people were required by law to keep their chimneys clean. Small boys did this very dirty work. Boys who were small enough to slip down the chimneys. They went through the streets crying:

> Sweep O! Patent sweep!
> Here's your patent sweeps!

They climbed to the roof tops, singing their chimney-cleaner's song. Then, with brush and scraper, they went down the chimney. After it was clean, and they were dirty, they took up their tools, their bags and buckets and scrapers and brushes, and went on, singing for new customers:

> Sweep your soot, ho!
> I am the man,
> That your chimney will clean
> If anyone can.

The broom men sang their wares. Brooms for thirteen cents each:

> Come buy a new brush
> Or a nice sweeping broom.
> 'Tis pleasant indeed
> To have a clean room.

And, of course, there was the milk man. Fresh milk every morning in the winter, and twice a day in the summer. They carried the milk in large tin kettles, in carts or on wagons, and it sold for four to six cents a quart. It was poured into the housewife's own container, right at her front door. Real service. As they went around town, up and down the streets, they sang:

> *Mee-lick! Mee-lick!*
>
> *Here's new milk from the cow,*
> *Which is so nice and fine*
> *That the doctors do say*
> *It is much better than wine.*

It was a noisy, musical place, the city was. These songs and others—the songs of the sellers of rushes for beds and mattresses; clean white sand from Rockaway for cleaning; fish and coal and clams and meat and lobsters; almost everything—were a part of the city.

There was singing and selling. And there was sighing too. Sighing by the Bowery B'hoys when Liza Stebbins sold her hot corn. She was a real Bowery gallus gal, as beautiful as her voice was sweet. Big, white roasting ears in a wooden bucket. She sang. How she sang! Hearts and taste buds worked fast:

Here's your nice hot corn!
Smoking hot! Piping hot!
What beauties I have got!

Here's smoking hot corn,
With salt that is nigh.
Only two pence an ear,
O pass me not by!

The Bowery B'hoys didn't pass her by. They bought her corn, and with ear in one hand and salt in the other they ate it as she went on, singing her song. Liza was Mose's special gallus gal. Some folks believe it was the hot corn that Mose ate that made him so big and strong.

Beautiful Dutch gardens brightened the quiet country lane way up north of Collect Pond. It soon became Fourteenth Street. Houses and more houses were built, and many people thought the houses would some day go to Twenty-Third Street, at least. Maybe farther.

More houses, More buildings. More businesses. More fires!

Always there was fire. Ready to destroy what men

32

had built. Fire. A good servant, but a bad master.

Always there were the volunteer firemen. And there was Mose!

He was big, Mose was. Seven feet tall, some say. Others say he was so big he could sit around a table all by himself. The hands at the ends of his arms made fists the size of Jersey hams. And his feet! There are those who say his feet were as big as East River barges.

Nonsense! Nothing of the kind. Mose was big all right. But his feet were not that big. If they were, he could never have pulled the *White Ghost* down some of New York's narrow streets.

His feet were ordinary size, considering the man. All the loose talk about barges probably comes from a simple fact. That stems from the time two boys, small boys they were, found one of his old boots. They used it as their ship when they played pirate on Sunfish Pond. No sense in talking about East River barges. Sunfish Pond wasn't big enough for a barge. Besides, the boys carried the boot up to Sunfish Pond and that was way up north, below Murray Hill. Near Peter Cooper's glue factory. It couldn't have been very big, or they couldn't have carried it that far. Anyway, there wasn't much room to spare

33

when the two boys got in and used his boot for their boat. And they were small boys, remember.

Whatever question there may have been about the size of Mose's boots, there is no doubt about the fact that they were strong. Extra strong since the day Mose forgot himself in a rush to answer the fire bell. He pulled his boots on that day. Didn't jump into them as he sometimes did. He was pulling them on, and he didn't stop pulling in time, and he pushed his feet right through the soles.

His hard leather fire helmet was the size of a vinegar barrel. The shirt he wore was bright red. That was the badge of a fireman. It was double-breasted and the buttons were white. His hair was red too. Not the same red as the shirt. But red nevertheless. It was plastered down tight, like paper to a wall, and it shone like the ice on Kips Bay on a moonlit night. Slick and neat, it draped over his forehead. Shaped in sweeping points, it swooped low in handsome curves before each ear toward the blue of his eyes.

"Soap locks" they called them then. The fashionable nobs from Broadway plastered their hair down with soap to firmly hold the locks in place. Mose's

flaming thatch was not to be tamed by soap. Mose
and the Bowery B'hoys used bear grease, firmer stuff
by far. If bear grease could hold a bear together,
little wonder it could subdue Mose's wiry mane and
hold it firmly in place.

The clamps of his galluses were brass and in the
shape of a double eagle. American bald eagles, they
were. And in their beaks the eagles held a copper
ribbon. And on the ribbons were the words en-
graved:

Lady Washington, Engine No. 40.

The letters were bold. No matter. There was room
to spare. The galluses and the double-eagle clasps
were the badge of a fireman too. There could be no
doubt about it. Mose was a fireman. Every inch of
him.

He used a butcher's cleaver for a pocket knife.
When the Lady Washington Guards marched off
for a shooting match or a day in the country, he hung
a barrel of golden New York ale at his belt.

His jacket was a short, dark coat. A pea jacket.
He wore it, or carried it rakishly over his arm, as
the weather required.

35

A Long Nine segar pointed dangerously at his eye. Two foot long it was. And once when he ran to a fire he carefully put it down on a stone wall. The neighbors saw it, and called a fire engine to put it out. Quite a job it was for them to do it too. On winter days, the Bowery B'hoys gathered around Mose, not only to soak up some of the glory that reflected from him, but also for the heat from the Long Nine segar.

On top of Mose, crowning the mighty man, was a plug hat. A tall beaver hat, somewhat battered, as befitted a veteran of fights and fires. The hat was carefully tilted down on his forehead. It balanced nicely over his left eye, neatly counterbalancing the menacing angle of the Long Nine segar.

By trade, he was a printer. He worked on Mr. Beach's *Sun*. A good printer he was, too. Such a man could scarcely be expected to set ordinary type. So, in keeping with his size, Mose set the type for the headlines. And often he made the news that made the headlines.

The Volunteer Fire Department of Little Old New York was born on December 3, in 1731. That was the day two Newsham fire engines were unloaded from the ship *Beaver*. Fresh from England they were, for no factory or shop in America could make such fine machines. In that year the Volunteer Fire Department protected 8,628 people and 1,200 houses.

New York was quite a town even then. It was a busy trading center. For a long time the law had required hay and straw to be kept at a distance from the houses and the streets. Quite a few streets were paved with pebblestones. Fine streets they were, sloping in toward the center.

Since 1697, the streets had been lighted at night. In the winter every householder was required to put a light in his window facing the street. And not only that. A "lanthorn & Candle" were hung out on a pole before "Every Seaventh house in the severall Wards of this Citty." The cost of this luxury was borne by the inhabitants of the seven houses equally. Naturally, this was not necessary all the time and was done only "in the Darke time of ye Moon in the Winter season."

There had always been fires, even before the Newsham engines came. But there had been the men to fight them. One year after Peter Stuyvesant arrived in New Amsterdam he appointed four fire wardens to inspect the houses and chimneys. And there was a heavy fine of three guilders for every chimney unswept or in ill repair.

Two of the wardens were Dutchmen and two were Englishmen. There could be no unfairness in the appointments to such an important post. But the town was Dutch then, and the wardens were called *brandt meisters*. That was in 1648. The wardens served almost a thousand people, and there were 120 houses.

And there was a law too. There is always a law against evil, and fire was evil, as everyone knew. Each house must have a leather fire bucket at the door, always ready. The Rattle Watch prowled the streets at night, always alert for the first small, cruel flame. "Prowlers," they were called. They summoned the citizens to fight a fire by sounding their rattles—wooden ratchet devices on a stick. The rattles made sounds loud enough to drown out the snoring of the sleepiest Dutchman.

At the sound of the rattles, the sleepy citizens threw their buckets into the street where they could be picked up with no delay and put to use. Then, when the good burghers got into their pantaloons and boots, they rushed out to fight the fire. They picked up the first bucket they could find and hurried toward the blaze.

They formed a line from the water to the fire, and another line from the fire back to the water. There were cisterns at the churches and other public buildings for this purpose. There were wells also. And, of course, there were the ponds and brooks and the East River and the Hudson.

The leather buckets were filled with water and passed from hand to hand. After the water was thrown on the fire, the empty buckets were passed back, down the second line, for more water. Women took their places in the lines. Children too, if they were big enough. Fire was everybody's enemy.

When it was all over, the buckets were taken to City Hall on Wall Street where they could be claimed by their owners.

Almost a century after Peter Stuyvesant and his *brandt meisters,* when the Newsham engines were hauled up the streets, the paint and brass caught many an eye and stole many a heart. There was no end of eager hands to pull at the ropes, and lift the machines around the corners, for the axles were fixed solidly to the machines. Small matter. They had wheels. They rolled. They were brightly painted

and the brass around the air chamber glistened welcome and mystery.

As many as twenty men could work the brakes, the handles that moved the pumps. Men were needed to carry the water in leather buckets. But not to throw it on the fire. That is what the machine was for. The water was dumped into the machine's tank, and the pumps forced it out through the pipe in a long, slender stream, to fly against the flames.

This was the very latest engine to fight fire. But some mumbled and grumbled at the expense. Others thought Zachary Greyaal's invention would have been better. Fasten gunpowder in a case to a barrel of water and roll the barrel into the burning building. The heat would make the powder explode. Blooey! A barrel of water exploded all over the fire. The fire was out. It was all over. But most people seemed to think that might be a little bit dangerous.

The engines won out. The first Volunteer Fire Company was formed. Then the second. Then the third, with an engine made in America. Then, there were many, many more. Social, political, and business leaders were members. Working men, clerks and mechanics. Men from all walks of life who had something of the hero in them and a desire to help their neighbors. Danger had to be met face to face and fire was danger.

The Newsham machines were taken to their new sheds at the City Hall at Broad and Wall Streets. Near by was the famous buttonwood tree that sheltered the merchants and traders as they transacted their business in its shade. This was the beginning of the New York Stock Exchange.

It was the same famous street corner where John Peter Zenger, the publisher of the New York *Weekly Journal,* was tried in court and successfully fought his great legal battle for the right of freedom of the press. It was the same historic corner where George Washington took his oath of office as the first President, in 1789.

A fitting place for the city's first fire engines.

The years passed. The Revolutionary War came. The New York volunteer firemen left their jobs and their engines and followed General Washington as he retreated from Brooklyn after the Battle of Long Island.

A few days later, the city was in flames. British soldiers were not firemen. The flames roared through the city and destroyed one quarter of it. The fire burned across the town below Wall Street from the

East River to the Hudson, and then it stormed along the shore of the Hudson. It destroyed everything in its path to Chambers Street where the buildings stopped, and where the countryside began.

And on that flaming night, September 21, 1776, Nathan Hale was captured. He was taken to Beekman Mansion, several miles north of the city on the East River, and tried as a spy. The next morning, the smoke of the great fire floated over Nathan Hale as he stood on the gallows and said, "I only regret that I have but one life to lose for my country."

Homeless people lived out the war in a "Canvastown." Ships' sails were made into shelters at the skeletons of burned-out chimneys.

The volunteer firemen fought out the war. Far away from their beloved engines, they yearned for the time when they might return and fight the old enemy, fire.

Sykesey

⟨ IN WHICH *Sykesey is introduced, together with some other members of* Lady Washington Engine Company No. 40; *Sykesey's attempts to be like Mose, humorous and well-nigh tragic; a man in danger; Mose to the rescue; "Man the ropes!"; "Sykesey, take the butt!"; a hard-headed hot head; "A little fire is easier to put out than a big one"; a novel invention; "The easiest fire to handle is one that never gits started at all."*

THE war ended seven years later. On November 25, 1783, the volunteer firemen marched down Bowery Lane. They found a war-torn city. Their beloved engines were damaged and rusty. The fire-fighting groups they found were a sorry lot. Inex-

45

perienced, with poor direction, they had sought, in a small, ineffective way, to protect property from fire. Their names were "Friendly Union," "Hand in Hand," and "Heart in Hand." Names that spoke of co-operation. They were friendly groups, but they did not know how to fight fires.

The volunteer firemen reorganized. The rebuilding of the machines began, as did the rebuilding of the city. The war of guns was over, but the war against fire went on.

Hose was made of leather then, and was sewn together. The seams broke and more water went on the men than on the fire. Riveted hose was yet to come. It was a slow process, but a way was being found to suck the water into the engine box. The heavy two-and-a-half-gallon leather buckets would soon be gone.

The years passed. The first hydrant was installed. It was wood. It was crude. But it was a long step in the battle against fire. The first one was installed at the corner of Liberty and William Streets, in 1807. It would be many years before fire plugs would be in general use throughout the city. Fire plugs. That's what they were called. That's what they were. Wooden plugs in water mains made of logs.

Mose remembered the big policemen and the big copper badges they wore. The copper badges gave to policemen the name "cops."

While Mose was growing up, others were growing up too. When an old fireman lost his life in flames or under the ruins of a burning building, a young man stood forth to take his place. When old muscles gave out and old shoulders could no longer bear the weight of fire fighting, youth came forward.

No, Mose was not alone; there were others. Hundreds of brave men were ready to fight fires with dozens of engines. *Lady Washington, Engine No. 40* had good men. There was Jim Jeroloman. He was a ship builder. Six foot four he stood. And great gold rings dangled from his ears. He had fought with "Yankee" Sullivan. Yankee whipped him, but Jim put up a great fight.

There was David Garthwaite. There was Orange County, and Jim Bard, and John Carlin.

And there was Sykesey. He was small, and an immigrant. One of the thousands, of the tens of thousands, who came to New York and made it home. A Bowery B'hoy with a big heart and a big love for *Lady Washington, Engine No. 40.*

There were others. Twenty-six in a company. And

47

hundreds of voluntary aids. Boys and young men. They were buffs or fans who one day hoped to be firemen, if they were good enough. Those who ran with the *Lady Washington* were called "Ghosts."

The first night Sykesey came to bunk in the fire house, he looked at the big hickory log Mose used for a pillow. His eyes lit up. The next night Mose smiled when he saw that Sykesey had a hickory log at the head of his bunk. Not as big as the log Mose used, but just as hard.

The fire bells rang that night. Mose tossed his shoes out the window. He pulled on his red shirt and jumped. Down like a flash of red lightning he went. As he hit the ground his feet slipped into the boots that had only then struck the pavement, and had not yet started bouncing.

He was ready. He opened the door. *Lady Washington, Engine No. 40* gleamed in the somber shadows as a ray of moonlight struck the gold of her trim little body.

The other volunteers were running up the street, down the street, answering the alarm, dropping everything, leaving their work, their play, their sleep. The fire bell was their command. Everything else was put aside. The other bunkers, the volunteers who slept on the second floor of the fire house, would soon be running down the stairs.

A woman stuck her head out of a window across the narrow way. A scream filled the air. Mose turned. The woman pointed to the fire-house window above his head. Men in the street stopped still and looked up.

Mose could not understand. Women screamed and men stopped to watch him. They had always done that. But he had already jumped. What were they looking at? He stepped back. Out into the middle of the street. He looked up. A flood of yellow moonlight poured over the roof tops and fell on the open window where he had stood only a short moment before. There was Sykesey. His shoes were in his hand. The brass double eagles on his galluses seemed to be flapping their wings wildly. Well they should, too, for it was clear that soon they would be in full flight.

Sykesey tightened his lips. "Don't jump!" Mose shouted.

It was too late. Sykesey was going to jump. He was going to do what Mose did if it was the last thing he ever did. The height of the window and the flint-hard roughness of the cobblestones made it

49

seem sure that it would indeed be Sykesey's last earthly act. Such a flight through space could serve only as practice for the new angel Sykesey seemed soon to become. The brass wings of the double eagles on his galluses could hold up a pair of pants, but they could never support the man himself in space.

Sykesey threw his boots. He paused for an appropriate splinter of time, as he had seen Mose do. Then he jumped after them. His light boots hit the cobblestones askew. They bounced and then fluttered about like the rumps of two gray ducks in Minetta Brook.

Would Sykesey also bounce when he hit? No man was quick enough to do anything, except one. Mose was there. He kept his eyes on Sykesey who, even though he was falling, certainly was bound for heaven. A light step back. Then forward. He moved as fast as the flip of a flounder's tail. His arms opened, and Sykesey entered his reach, and his firm embrace.

Sykesey's double eagles latched their wings onto Mose's double eagles. The galluses stretched and the fall was broken when Mose's arms tightened around the falling man.

Mose thrust Sykesey into the waiting boots. He stood there. On his face the look of terror changed to surprise. Real, buoyant, overwhelming surprise.

Mose turned to the engine. He opened the other door. He laid the drag ropes out and turned again. A look of pride was now on Sykesey's face. It quickly melted. Mose's great voice split the air.

"Here Sykesey," he shouted. "Man the ropes! Here, beside me." He held the rope out to Sykesey. The small one grabbed it. The other men reached the machine and seized the tongue and the ropes.

"Pull away!" Mose cried. "Pull away! Will you go now?" The *White Ghost* rumbled into the street.

"Where's the fire?" a man at the rear cried.

"Follow us," yelled Sykesey from his place beside Mose at the front end of the rope. Then he thought better of it. "Follow Mose," he shouted. "He'll find it. He can look in all directions at once. He's got an eye in the back of his head."

Down the street they went. At the corner, no pause. A turn to the right, for big Mose had seen the distant glow of a fire.

The *White Ghost* was first at the scene. She pulled up alongside a cistern. "Sykesey," said Mose, "take the butt!"

51

That was the prize for the second man to reach the engine. The heavy leather hose was unbuckled from the side of the engine, its end dumped into the water. Sykesey drew up the butt and screwed it into place.

"Man the brakes!" commanded Mose. A dozen men lined up on each side of the machine and seized the long wooden rods that worked the pumps.

The days of leather buckets had passed. A modern machine like the *White Ghost* sucked the water up into the tank, through the air chamber, and poured it out in a broad, steady stream. There was no longer the fixed metal pipe on top of the engine. There was a hose leading off two hundred feet, and the pipe, or nozzle, was on the end of the hose. A hose that could be taken into burning buildings, hauled upstairs, and dragged as close to the fire as a man could go.

The man who held the pipe was the first man at the engine after the alarm sounded. And that man was Mighty Mose.

The foreman came. He was late. Got his pants on backward in his rush in the dark. But he was there now. Just in time.

He held his brass speaking trumpet up to his

mouth and shouted: "At the brakes! Are you ready? Let her go!"

And the brakes crunched. The pistons moved and began to pound. The water rushed up and churned in the box. Mose hauled the hose forward, the pipe firm in his grip. Other men pulled the hose back of him. Its body thickened. The kinks snapped out straight, knocking over any man who was careless enough to stand in its way.

The water surged to the pipe. Its force pulled and jerked at Mose's arms like the kick of a mule. Mose held it steady and the stream fell on the fire.

It was a hot, bright fire. Without warning a huge burning timber broke loose and fell from the floor above. It landed on Mose's head and broke square in two. The ends shuddered at the impact. One end fell harmlessly. The other glanced against a near-by volunteer and struck him to the ground. He was dead.

Fire laddies came on the run and carried their fallen comrade away. Others turned to Mose. He did not have his heavy leather, brassbound helmet on, and they feared the worst.

"You all right, Mose?" asked Jim Bard.

53

"Yeah," said the big smoke-eater. "Just pick the burnin' coals out o' me hair." He grinned broadly. "I'll never muss again with any man that calls me hot headed. I ought to remember to wear me helmet whenever I'm fightin' a fire."

Sykesey and Jim brushed the burning embers out of his hair. Mose held the pipe steady. The fire was soon out. A steady stream of water in the right place. That's what it takes for fires.

They hauled the *White Ghost* home. She was cleaned and dried and shined. The wet hose was stretched out flat to dry and fresh hose was hung on the machine. The tools and equipment were checked, cleaned, and made ready for the next fire.

Mose drew Sykesey aside. "You shouldn't of done that," he said quietly.

"Vot?" asked Sykesey.

"Jumped like you done," Mose replied.

"But you done it," Sykesey said accusingly.

"I know it. But that ain't no sign you can."

"Vy not?"

How could Mose tell him that all men could not do what Mose did? Fortunately none of the other volunteers had tried it. But there would be very serious trouble if everyone started to jump out of windows when the fire bells rang.

"Because," he said, "if you ever fell on them cobblestones, you'd spatter so far you'd leave a grease spot about as big as a fly, that's why!"

Sykesey was not persuaded. "You done it. I seen you. If you can do it, I don't see vy I can't. You're heavier than me so you fall harder."

Mose wouldn't argue. He would find something more convincing. The next day he laid off work. He stayed in the fire house all day, except for a few visits to the metal works down the street.

The volunteers came that evening for their weekly meeting, to discuss the affairs of the company, and to talk about fires. As the men came upstairs into the bunkers' room, there were surprised and angry looks.

John Carlin exploded. "Mose," he said. "You shouldn't of done that. The corporation won't like it."

"You can't tear down a public building," said David.

"Vot iss it? Vot's it for?" asked Sykesey.

"It's to get to the masheen faster when the bells ring," said Mose. "I cut a hole in the floor an' put that brass pole right up t'rough it. Now we can slide

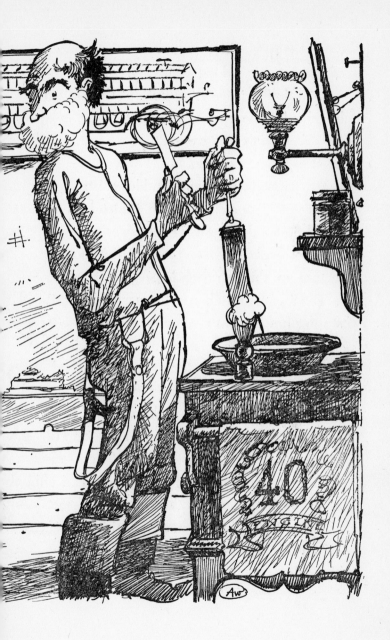

down the pole. There won't be no more jumpin' out of winders," he added pointedly.

"A little fire is easier to put out than a big one," he added. "The quicker you get to 'em, the smaller they are. That's why we got to move fast. An' here's what us bunkers can do!"

He stripped off his boots and his pants. He put his boots on the floor, side by side. He held his pants up and dropped the legs down, one over each boot. The garment folded down on the floor, the boot tops projecting up, through each leg.

The firemen watched with puzzled looks. But the strange process was made clear when Mose stepped back, took a running start, and jumped lightly into his boots. With a simple motion he reached down, lifted up his galluses, and slipped them over his shoulders. His pants and boots were on. That quick. He was ready. A step forward. He seized the new brass pole, and slid down it, out of sight.

"I vant to try it," shouted Sykesey, as a hubbub of eager shouting filled the air.

When Mose climbed back upstairs, everyone was busy jumping into pants and boots and sliding down the pole.

58

"Vell," said Sykesey. "*Enjine No. 40* vill always be foist at the fires now!"

"As long as there is fires," Mose said, "us firemen has to get to 'em fast to put 'em out. What would be best would be for everybody to be real careful so fires don't get started. The easiest fire of all to handle is the one that never gets started at all."

Mose with a Hose

❲ IN WHICH *a fire rages on a freezing night; the* Old
Maid *is passed; an unusual adventure in the snow; cold
iron and steel muscles; the enmity of the* Old Maid;
*"Sykesey, take the butt!"; Mose with a hose; a duck-
ing in the East River, close combat with fire, great
heat, and a shore dinner; "The corporation's prop'ty
is ruint!"; no thanks for a fireman.*

IT WAS a big fire. No need to peer down dark
streets for a faint, red glow. No need to search the
sky for a show of pink. The flames sprang far up
above the roof tops, stabbing through the blackness,
deep into the heart of heaven.

60

All over the city the fire bells were ringing. There was a deep, solemn command from St. Paul's steeple. Sharp insistence from the Fly Market bell. Strident instruction from the famous old Mechanics Bell at the East River shipyards. Deliberate orders from the belfry at City Hall. Dozens of iron tongues pounded out the warning that emerged from metal throats.

Hoarse and shrill. Deep and mellow. High and low. Slow and fast. All the bells of the city were at work that night. And their clamor shrieked out that the city was in danger. And the upward-springing barbs of wild heat, like the darting tongues of incandescent rattlesnakes, furnished endless exclamation marks for that word: *Danger!!*

A storm raged through the streets, and it was cold. Colder than the top of the North Pole in a January blizzard.

Fire engines from every part of town answered the alarm. The *White Ghost* skidded into the Bowery and sped through Chatham Square. There she met the *Old Maid, Engine No. 15.* The *Old Maid* was stalled in a snowdrift. Her men, straining to release their machine from the clutch of the snow, scowled and grumbled as the *White Ghost* slid past.

The little white-and-gold engine made the long

61

trip down Chatham and Nassau, toward Maiden Lane and the East River, where the fire raged. Mose, at the lead, plowed through snowdrifts, making a path for the men of *Lady Washington Engine Company No. 40,* and for the machine that crunched heavily through the snow behind them.

Suddenly the way before them was blocked! The narrow street in front of them was closed. The *Old Maid* pulled up behind.

"Vot iss it?" asked Sykesey.

"Don't know yet," said Mose. He pressed forward, pushing down the towering piles of snow. He peered over the top of the drift. "It's a stage coach," he said over his shoulder to the waiting volunteers.

"Vot's it doing there?"

"Got caught in the blizzard. In the middle of the street. There ain't enough room to go around. We got to git it out of the way."

The heavy omnibus was firmly trapped in the icy grasp of a snowdrift. Its tired team of horses stood helplessly between the traces. They blew hard from recent exertions and shivered mightily from the penetrating, piercing cold. Men were there with shovels, digging a path for the heavy stage. Mose

62

stepped closer. There was no time to stop and shovel snow.

"Unhitch the nags," he commanded. The driver hurried to follow his bidding. Mose led the horses to the side of the street, tramping down the drifts so they could follow.

No one questioned him, though some must have wondered how he was going to move the car without the horses. The exhausted animals gratefully edged up to the building. Great clouds of vapor throbbed through the icicles on their frosty noses.

Mose stepped back to the snowbound stage. He took hold of it and lifted. It did not budge. He squared his shoulders, took a deep breath and lifted again. It broke away from the hard-packed snow. He tucked it up further under his arms, and carried it to the side of the street, and put it down.

His left hand gripped the back wheel. When he tried to let go, he couldn't. His hand was frozen to the iron tire.

Sykesey saw it. The image of tragedy flashed in his mind. There would be a torn and bloody hand. Or a long delay while the metal was warmed enough to loosen its icy grip. . . .

63

"Hold on! Vait!" he shouted. "Ve got to heat it. Go git some hot vater!"

"No. Don't worry," said Mose. "I'll do it."

Mose twisted his wrist. The tendons on the back of his hand stood out in deep ridges. There was a rasping, cracking sound. The metal tire, brittle with cold, broke. Mose pulled his hand away. The metal that it covered came with it.

"Too bad to damage the stage company's prop'ty," he said, "but fires won't wait."

The street was clear now. He took up the drag rope again. "Are yez ready?" he cried.

"Ready!" shouted the volunteers of *Lady Washington Engine Company No. 40* with one voice.

"Pull away!" Once again the *White Ghost* moved down the white street.

The fire was in a warehouse at the water's edge. When they arrived it was a glowing inferno. Already the flying embers had found the stores across the street. Houses down the block were in danger. They would be next.

Engines from the neighborhood were there. Other fire companies were arriving, following the *Old Maid* in the path the *White Ghost* had made through the snow.

64

The *Old Maid's* men were called "Dock Rats" because of their habit of getting to the river's edge
before the other engines. But they were not first this
time. It galled them that the *White Ghost* had passed
their machine and reached the fire before they did.
They would not soon forget it.

Ice sealed the water at the shore line. Some engines had backed out on the river to the edge of the
ice and dropped their suction hoses in the water
there. Other companies had cut holes in the ice
closer to shore.

Mose led the engine to the East River shore. He
stepped out on the ice. "Be careful, Mose," said Sykesey. "That ice froze with the slippery side up."

The ice was as solid as the frozen, rocky shore.
Mose waved Sykesey and the others back. He
stamped his hobnailed heel down on the glassy surface. Then he jumped up and his boots came down
with a crash. Chips flew out in all directions. The
ice cracked and broke, and Mose fell through. Water
splashed up. The men dodged back out of the way.
In the scramble, the ducking of heads, the blinking
of eyes, no one could be sure what happened. He
moved faster than a sparrow in an alley full of
hungry cats. It was all over as quick as the snap of

65

your fingers. And when it was over, there was Mose on the shore. And he was dry.

"Now look at that, vill you?" demanded Sykesey. "He fell in that vater, an' he got out so fast he didn't even git vet!"

Mose put a stop to such non-fire-fighting observations. "Sykesey," he said, "take the butt!"

Sykesey sprang to work. Men lined up at the brakes. There was the rasping sound of heavy, riveted, leather hose resisting in the cold. The splash of the suction pipe. The clang of spanners on icy brass. The hoarse voices through speaking trumpets. The shouts of eager men. The bang of brakes. The clang of pumps. The surge and hiss of water and air. Mose carried the pipe to the blaze, dragging the hose behind him.

This was hand-to-hand fighting. Uncontrolled flames against a man. His enemy could fight in every direction. An octopus of flame, with restless, searching arms, each able to sear the flesh. It was all lethal. All of it. From its hot, flaming heart to the tip of its incandescent talons, and beyond. For its breath was deadly, and its smothering, swirling smoke could kill.

A man against a raging flame. A stream of water was his weapon. One thin, hard stream of water. It sped with a rush to its goal and found its mark. With a hiss of agony it was transformed into steam and flooded upward, carried away by clouds of smoke.

The wind changed. It caught the water in mid-air in the heart of the blaze. Now, a scalding, steaming shower blew back in his face. Hot ashes, sparks, and spears of flame followed.

Mose moved to the left. Down the slope of the river bank. The flames stabbed after him. The thin ice, near the fire, broke at the touch of his feet. He waded out into the frigid stream. The fire could not reach him now. The stream from the pipe sprayed against the blaze. He slipped, and fell in the water. Quickly he regained his footing. The water was up to his waist.

"Look at that feller," said Sykesey. "Bein' in that water don't seem to bother him none." He shivered. "I'm standin' on dry land, an' I'm colder than a polar bear's nose."

The wind changed again. Mose came out of the river. Now he could once more approach the fire. Closer. Closer. He moved toward the flame.

The Ghosts stayed at the brakes. Never for an instant did the steady stream of water fail or falter.

Other companies were fighting in other quarters.

People shivering with cold stood across the street, watching. Anxiety was on every face. At the windows, in the houses, others shivered with fear. Terror was on the faces.

Mose advanced slowly. He held the pipe steady, always aimed at the scorching heart. A heart that moved. That grew big and wild. Small and intense. Never still. Always changing. Mose moved his hands back to the leather hose. The brass pipe poked its nose closer to the fire. If the water could keep playing on those vital spots, the fire would soon be out.

The flaming heart rose and fell. It moved and turned. No matter what deceit or trick or strategem, Mose advanced.

"Look!" cried Sykesey. "His vet clothes is steaming!"

It was true. A cloud of steam enveloped him.

"Why not?" the foreman said. "It's hot enough where Mose is to melt a rock."

Hot enough to melt a rock. Perhaps so. Perhaps not. But it was hot enough to melt the metal pipe. Slowly the nozzle grew limp and bent down like a thin sucked stick of soft licorice candy on a hot day.

The stream of water fell short of the flame. The men at the brakes worked harder. The thrust of the

68

pistons beat against the air chamber and the water throbbed like the pulse of an angry mastodon. At each surge the melting pipe, limber as an eel, moved in involuntary, random circles, and the water missed the fire.

The fire grew with a new strength and its heat beat against the fear-struck faces across the street. The pain of cold changed to the pain of heat, and the crowd moved back.

A flood of molten brass oozed to the end of the dancing pipe where glowing drops sprayed out beyond the steaming hot water to build new fires.

The Fire Commissioner was there. "Mose should back away from that fire," he said.

The foreman raised his metal speaking trumpet. He dropped it. It was hot. He put on his heavy leather gloves and held it to his mouth. "Back away! Back away, Mose!" he shouted.

Mose stood his ground. "That's insubordination," the Commissioner growled.

"I don't t'ink he can hear," said Sykesey, shouting above the roar of flames and brakes and water and panting, grunting men.

"Back away! Back away!" The order blasted from the trumpet again.

69

The brass pipe quit its loose writhing. It melted off, fell to the ground, a glowing glob, and flattened out like a pancake. The molten metal trickled in a shining stream toward the fire. The hard, tight, flying stream was gone. Water gurgled in a wide, loose flow from the open mouth of the hose. Now he would have to back away. But no. Not yet. Mose put his big thumb over the end. The loose flow stopped. The hose grew taut again. And a long, hard stream slid past his thumb. It cut through the smoke and sprang through the heat to the blaze.

He held it there. The water did its work. Death came to the blaze. Black smoke faded and white steam took its place. Mose turned away.

"You all right?" asked Sykesey.

"Yeah," said Mose. "Kinda hot, though. An' tired, too. An' hungry."

He sat down on the curb. His clothes were hot and steaming. If they had not been wet, they would long since have burst into flame. The others gathered around. The *White Ghost* stood silent, her white and gold shadowed by a film of ashes, smoke, and mud.

Down the street the other volunteer companies were still fighting. But the Ghosts, the men of *Lady*

Washington Engine Company No. 40, could rest for a moment.

"Vimmin are coming vit coffee an' samwitches," said Sykesey.

"Good," said Mose. "But I can eat more than coffee an' samwitches."

He put his hand in his steaming jacket pocket. "What's this?" he exclaimed. He drew his hand from his pocket and looked at it incredulously. He held a lobster. A red, steaming, boiled lobster.

"Vhere did that come from?" demanded Sykesey.

"Guess he must of got inside me pocket when I was in the river," said Mose. "Then when I got up close to the fire where it was nice an' hot, he must of got himself all boiled real nice."

He got up from the curb and put the lobster on a packing case. Now, both hands went into his pockets. "All right, lads," he announced. "Dinner's on me!" and he pulled out two more lobsters. And then two more.

Further exploration brought forth six shad from the deep depths of the breast pockets of his red fireman's shirt. Twenty-three well-boiled mackerel came from the cavernous side pockets where he carried the butcher's cleaver he used as a pocket knife.

And five flounder had packed themselves neatly in the flat confines of each hip pocket.

"A real shore dinner," exclaimed David.

"All except the clams," amended Sykesey, who knew about shore dinners.

Mose looked down. A smile appeared on his face. "The world is full of surprises," he said. "An' it looks like we got clams, too!"

He slipped out of his long fireman's boots. He held one upside down over the packing case. A wave of hot, steaming clams slid out. Then another, from the other boot.

Two bright tame fires warmed the hungry group as the men clustered around the packing case. Linda, the beautiful segar girl, and Liza Stebbins, Mose's special Bowery gallus girl, came with hot coffee and sandwiches. There was a time for fighting fires. There was a time too for warm food and a little rest to prepare for more fire fighting.

"It iss surprising in a vay," said Sykesey between bites. "But, in another vay, it ain't."

"Ain't what?" asked Mose.

"Surprising," Sykesey said. "Moses and the Children of Israel received manna from Heaven ven they vas in the vilderness."

74

"An' we git a hot shore dinner from the East River," Mose added.

"That's right."

New York's rivers had fed the city for two centuries. They would continue to supply the city with the means of life for centuries to come. Not always and forever with unexpected shore dinners. But with the means to transport the materials for dinners of all kinds, and the food for factories too, and industry, and trade.

There were hungry men at that fire on the East River. There were two pretty girls. And there was one angry Fire Commissioner.

The Fire Commissioner looked serious. His chin was buried in the fat folds of his neck. "Mose!" he barked.

"Yeah?" answered Mose, lobster claw in hand.

"You are in trouble!"

"Trouble? Why?"

"For melting that pipe."

Interest in food bowed to interest in melted pipes. The men around the packing case paused and listened.

"What do you mean?"

"You deliberately went too close to the fire. You

75

were insubordinate when your foreman ordered you to back away. And you deliberately went ahead and melted the pipe off of your hose." The Commissioner folded his arms. His lips tightened and his chin jutted out feebly above his pudgy jowls.

A volunteer fireman didn't ask for thanks. He rarely got it. Fire fighting, like virtue, was its own reward. The men were awed when they saw the pipe melt and drop from Mose's hands. And they were proud. They had never imagined that anyone would find fault.

"Now, Mr. Commissioner," Jim Jeroloman interrupted, "the city can't expect that fire-fightin' equipment won't be damaged—"

"Damaged?" exploded the Commissioner. "Harrumph! Damaged, you say? That pipe ain't damaged! It's destroyed! Completely destroyed! The corporation's property is ruined!"

"The corporation's prop'ty is ruint!" mimicked Sykesey disdainfully. "Ruint? Damaged? Destroyed? Vot's the diff'rence?" he demanded, shaking a long finger under the Commissioner's fat nose.

"I only done me dooty," said Mose.

"That is open to very serious question. Very serious. The city may not think a volunteer fireman has

76

a duty to melt a pipe. Anyway, your willful disregard of the orders and the regulations has caused a loss to the corporation of one good brass pipe! Harrumph!"

"Sometimes ve got to buy erl for the lanterns. An' even grease for the vheels. The city sometimes doesn't give us paint for the masheen. So ve buy a pipe if ve got to. So vot? The city ought to give Mose a gold metal, an' hang up that melted brass pipe in the office of the Common Council!" Sykesey punctuated his remarks by tossing a lobster tail in the fire.

As the discussion involved neither fires, fights, frolics, nor food, it did not hold Mose's attention. "Why don't yez have something to eat, Mr. Commissioner?" he asked.

"I don't fancy eating food that has been cooked in a man's clothes," said the Commissioner sharply.

"Don't hurt it a bit," Mose replied. "Jest think of Mrs. Murphy's chowder. Somebody put the overalls in it, an' everybody sings about it."

The Commissioner grimaced and turned away. "Now b'hoys," said Mose. "We had our lunch. An' we had a good rest. The fire's still boinin'."

He turned to the Commissioner. "Mr. Commissioner," he said, "these b'hoys an' me is goin' to fight the fire. Foller us close an' see if any more of the corporation's prop'ty is ruint."

Mose grew solemn for a moment. His thoughts went back to a time when he was a small boy. "Come on, lads. We got some more fightin' to do," he said. "An' remember, don't let it bother you none if you have some bad luck, or if you lose. You can't win all the time!"

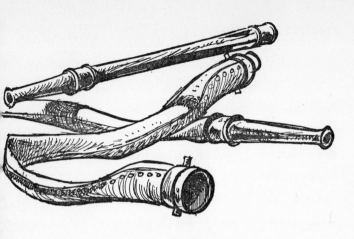

The "Old Maid"

⟦ IN WHICH *three engines form a line to fight fire; speed, hardship, and danger; one large engine and two small ones; "Man the brakes!"; the cruel plan of the Old Maid; the tables turned; a washing; a burning building and a battering ram; the tables turned again; "the Old Maid will get even!"; "the bigger they are, the harder they fall."*

THE blaze had spread. Several blocks were in flames. Streams of water were pouring into the burning buildings from every direction. To pump water, the engines worked in lines. One of the lines was formed by the *White Ghost,* the *Old Maid,* and the *Red Rover.*

79

Water was to be pumped from the river by the *White Ghost*. It would be forced through her hose to the *Old Maid*. The *Old Maid* would pump it on, through its own hose, another 200 feet to the waiting box of the *Red Rover*. And from the *Red Rover* to the fire.

Lines like this sometimes stretched a mile or more from the water to the fire. Often as many as twenty or more engines in line. Each one depending on the other. If one machine failed in its share of the work, the water box ahead would soon be empty and there would be no water for the fire. Disgrace and shame came to the company that failed to keep water in the box ahead.

Each machine pumped the water out as fast as the engine behind pumped it in. If it did not, if the water overflowed its tank, it was "washed." And to be washed was a disgrace. Strong men, weak and exhausted from their work at the brakes, might fall to the ground in tears if such a tragedy befell their machine.

Each company worked with each other, and against each other. And they all worked against the fire.

The brakes were usually worked at the rate of

sixty strokes each minute. But not always. The speed of the stroke varied with the need to move the water on toward the fire. When the need was great—to keep from being washed or pumped dry—or to wash or dry up another machine—the brakes were played faster. As fast as 130, or even 170 strokes a minute. A stroke up and down, once, twice, or even three times every second. Strength and speed! That's what it took!

The foreman counted and set the speed for the brakes to work. He shouted through his speaking trumpet to be heard above the noise of fire, machines, and men. "One, two, three, four." He encouraged them. "All together. Work her lively, men. Every one." He shamed them. "You don't half work." He challenged them. "Stave her sides in." He praised them. "Now you've got her."

Twenty to forty men manned the brakes at each machine. It was back-breaking, heart-breaking work. A man could keep it up only a few minutes. When he had worked to exhaustion, when he stopped to rest and catch his breath, another took his place at the machine.

Crushed fingers, cracked heads, and broken bones were the reward of the careless man who got in

81

the way of the moving brakes. Look sharp. Be quick. Work hard. Those were the rules.

The *Red Rover, Engine No. 34,* was a famous machine and a great fire fighter. In later years she was to bear the name of *Howard,* after the renowned Harry Howard, who became the Chief Engineer of the New York Fire Department.

The *Old Maid* was big. She had a long history. She was Engine No. 15 in the corporation's records. She was known as the *Peterson Engine* in honor of her foreman who died in the great fire of 1811. Because of the beautiful floral design on her back panel she was also known as *Wreath of Roses.*

Her box was made of polished rosewood. Her company was proud and famous, for in all her years the *Old Maid* had never been washed. And no company had washed more machines than she. And there she stood, powerful and proud, waiting to take water from the *White Ghost,* two hundred feet away.

"Will you give us water?" the *Old Maid's* foreman asked through his speaking trumpet.

"Sykesey, take the butt," said Mose calmly.

"An' keep it comin'!" There was a sneer in the voice.

82

"Plenty of it!" The "Bloods" and "Fly-by-Nights," *Old Maid* runners, nudged each other and winked. Their big engine would out-pump the *White Ghost*. No doubt about it.

"Water comin'!" the *White Ghost*'s foreman replied. He turned to the Ghosts. "Stand by your brakes, men," he said.

"Keep us full!" There was a taunt in the words.

"Man the brakes," the foreman said. The *White Ghost* company lined up and grasped the long wooden rods.

"Are you ready?"

"Ready!"

"Then go. One, two, three, four." The men strained and the long brakes began to move. Up and down. Up and down.

"Every one of you. One. Two. Three. Four," shouted the leader. "Work her lively, lads."

Water came into her box from the river. The hose began to charge. Slowly it began to fill, and the water started on its long trip to the *Old Maid*.

"Water! We want water!" cried the Dock Rats standing beside the *Old Maid*. The men laughed and joked. The little *White Ghost* could never supply water as fast as the *Old Maid* could pump it on to the *Red Rover*.

The water bubbled into the *Old Maid*'s box. Her men began to work the brakes. They would pump their box dry. They would bring shame to the *White Ghost*. It was easy. Too easy. Like taking candy from a baby.

Mose and the Ghosts understood. They knew the *Old Maid* would never be content to pump just enough water on to the *Red Rover*. They would work hard and pump their box dry. Disgrace for the *White Ghost*. Glory for the *Old Maid*. Then they would let their box fill up to her rosewood top. They would pump fast. In a rush. And they would wash the *Red Rover*. Disgrace for the *Red Rover*. More glory for the *Old Maid*.

Almost a thousand men and boys ran with the *Old Maid*. They were the buffs, the fans. "Bloods" and "Fly-by-Nights," they called themselves. Even on such a cold night as this, hundreds of her runners were there, and they would take places at the brakes if they were needed.

And in the stores, on the street corners, and in the warehouses, from the Battery to 14th Street, in Five

Points and the Bowery, they would slap their hips with glee. They would laugh. And they would tell over and over again how they dried up the *White Ghost* and washed the *Red Rover*.

They would tell the story on Broadway, Chatham Square, Hanover Square, Centre Market, all over town! It would be a long, never-ending joke, and the *Old Maid* would be the victor and the greatest fire engine in the world. And the men of the *White Ghost* and the *Red Rover* would go down the back streets. They would stay away from street corners. But they would wait for another chance to dry up the *Old Maid*, to wash the *Old Maid*. It would be a small chance. A hopeless chance. For the *Old Maid* was big. But until they did, they would hear the jokes, the story, the laughter. Always the laughter. Always. Always.

It was no secret. The *Old Maid* was between two small engines. One was white and gold. The other was red. It was the chance of a lifetime.

"Oh, you *White Ghost!* We'll dry you up!" the Dock Rats shouted.

The Ghosts, who ran with the *Lady Washington*, looked up the street at the Bloods and Fly-by-Nights.

They looked at their beloved *White Ghost*, and they wondered if she could keep up with the big machine.

"Oh, you, *Red Rover!* Look out! We're goin' to wash you!" the Dock Rats cried.

The Rovers knew. They wondered. And they hoped.

Water from the *Old Maid* reached the *Red Rover*. The brakes on the *Red Rover* began to work. Water spat at the fire through a third-story window. That was what they were all working for. That is what they all should have been working for. Water on the fire. But the *Old Maid* was working for something else. To dry up the *White Ghost!* To wash the *Red Rover!*

Mose was resolved that the *Old Maid* would not dry up the *White Ghost*. "Sykesey," he said, "tell you what to do. I'll take one side of the masheen. You keep as many of the lads on the other side as yez can. We'll fill up the *Old Maid's* box. Then I'll go an' help those lads on the *Red Rover*."

And so it was. Mose on one side of the engine. And the rest of the company on the other side. No envy or jealousy there. Every man worked with a will. *Lady Washington Engine No. 40* would not be pumped dry if they could help it. Not even by the big, powerful, proud *Old Maid*. Not even if she did have a polished rosewood box. Not if strong hearts and strong backs and willing hands could work for the little white-and-gold engine standing small and alone at the river's edge.

Mose knew they were winning. He heard the foreman's cries from the *Old Maid*. "Work, men! Will you work now? Faster! Harder! Stronger! She's filling up on us!"

This was good news for the Ghosts. They worked at the brakes even harder. Mose on one side. The rest of the company on the other. From the *Old Maid* came more urgent words. "Faster, men! Faster! She's a-fillin' up! Stave her sides in!"

"Good work, b'hoys. Steady an' hard. Steady an' hard. Now you've got her. Keep it up. Keep it up." Mose's words were quiet, confident.

"Faster! Faster! Faster!" The strident cries from the *Old Maid* were desperate. Bloods and Fly-by-Nights were falling to the ground, exhausted.

But it was too late now. More speed would not help. Water flooded out of the *Old Maid*'s rosewood

87

box. It splashed and flooded down her shining sides. She was washed! The *White Ghost* had washed the *Old Maid!*

"Man this side," cried Mose. A dozen men took the brake Mose had been working.

"I'm a-goin' to help the *Red Rover,*" he said.

He walked past the *Old Maid*. He was greeted with sullen, angry looks. "Good work, *Old Maid,*" he said. "You pumped us dry—almost." Then he hurried on.

The *Red Rover* was an old friend of the *White Ghost*. But Mose was interested only in his own machine. Each engine had to fight its own battles. What he really wanted to do was to get up close to the fire. When he got there, it was clear that water in the third-story window was not reaching the vital spot. The fire was below, on the first floor. But no windows were there. Nothing but a hard, solid, brick wall.

"We got to break through that wall," said the Chief Engineer.

"But first we got to move them two trees standin' at the curb," said the Assistant.

"Yes," said the Chief. "Get men with axes."

"Don't need no axes," said Mose. "I'll move the

trees." He walked up to the trees that blocked the way. Leaning down, he grasped the smaller one firmly, and pulled. The roots cracked and the tree came up. He tossed it aside. Then he turned to the other and pulled it up too.

Now there was space in which to work. The Chief directed the men. Twenty men on a long pole. A battering ram. Crash! Once again! Crash! Up against the wall. Once more! Crash! The pole splintered. It was useless.

"Get a bigger pole!" commanded the Chief. "We got to break a hole through that wall!" But there was no bigger pole.

"Chief," said Mose, "I think I can break a hole t'rough them bricks."

"How?"

"Put six men on the pipe. T'ree on each side," said Mose.

"What good will that do?" asked the Chief.

"You're the Chief. This ain't me own company," Mose said. "But if yez do as I say, I'll try to bust a hole t'rough the wall."

"Well, Mose, if you say so, we'll try it." The Chief knew no one could fight fires like Mose. "Six men take the pipe!" he commanded.

89

"Now," said Mose, "I'll take one of the brakes, an' all the rest of yez can take the other."

The *Old Maid* had been pumping hard. The *Red Rover*'s box was almost full. Soon it would flow over the top, and the *Red Rover* would be washed.

The Chief issued the commands. Men crowded up to the brake. Mose reached for the other. "Now hold the stream against the wall," he said.

Six men at the pipe looked back. They were puzzled. "Against the wall?"

The Chief was puzzled, too, but he thundered the command through his silver speaking trumpet. "Against the wall!"

"Now keep up with me," said Mose to the men across the machine at the other brake. He lifted up. Pulled down. Up again. Down. The *Red Rover* Company on the other side went to work too. Their engine was almost washed. Something must be done!

"Will you work now?" cried Mose. Yes. They would. With a will. They might still keep her from being washed. Muscles strained.

The pipe kicked as the water reached it. The stream played straight ahead against the brick wall. Six men set their muscles. They held on. Held it steady.

"Work, now!" cried Mose. "Keep with me." The brakes groaned and crunched. The pressure stepped up. The flow of water increased. It came out of the pipe with a roar. The glow of fire struck it, and it looked like a painted post. A rainbow stretched out straight. The Rovers pushed and pulled at the brake as Mose worked at the other.

The pressure increased. A hard, tight stream pushed out of the pipe, harder, faster, tighter. Six men struggled at the pipe and held it firm. The stream beat against the brick wall like a steel rod. A piece of brick chipped off. Then another fell away. Another shattered where the force of the water struck. A small hole appeared. Water beat at the edges. Chips of bricks flew like sparks from a grindstone. The hole grew larger.

"Fight the fire! At it! Closer!" Mose commanded. Six men advanced to the looming hole and the water fell on the fire inside. The brakes worked on and on. The water did its work. It was over. The fire was out.

Then the hose grew limp. There was no water in the box. A shout went up from the *Red Rover*. "It's the *Old Maid!* We've dried her up! We've dried her up!"

They cheered and they danced. The Ghosts shouted with the Rovers. But two hundred feet away the *Old Maid* was working hard. The men worked the brakes, standing in water that had been washed over their machine by the *White Ghost* only a few moments before.

Grunts and groans and angry words came from the *Old Maid*. The big, powerful *Old Maid* with a polished rosewood box had been washed. She had been dried up. All in one night. All at one fire. Her pride and her arrogance were gone. But anger was there. The Dock Rats knew that Mose's great strength had beaten them. The Bloods and the Fly-by-Nights knew too. They would remember. The *Old Maid* would get even. She would have revenge. You bet your life she would!

Mose looked at her beaten men and he saw the dark scowls and the burning hate. "The *Old Maid* will git even. You can bet high on that," a Dock Rat muttered.

The Ghosts and the Rovers gathered around Mose and cheered. "The *Old Maid* is big, and she had a big pride," he said. "It's all right to cheer when you win, especially when you win out over a big one. Because, the bigger they are, the harder they fall. But don't never forget, you can't win all the time."

Linda, the Beautiful Segar Girl

⟦ IN WHICH *a high fire burns and danger threatens in a narrow street; a cry of distress; Mose to the rescue; a flaming threat and a remarkable feat at a towering height; five tender human lives in danger; "We was scairt, but we ain't no more"; Linda, the beautiful segar girl; a heroic rescue; thanks for a fireman; "I only done me dooty!"*

THAT wall is goin' to fall," exclaimed the foreman.

"Yes," said the Chief anxiously. "The first two floors is almost gone."

"And the flames is spreadin' up. The third floor is goin' fast. The fourth floor will soon be burnin'," the foreman added.

He looked anxiously at his men. They were in close quarters. The *Lady Washington* Company was in a narrow street. Four-story houses on either side of the street, rising straight up from the sidewalks, made a slender, brick-walled canyon.

Water from the hose arched through the third-story window. Flames lashed back. Smoke billowed up.

"We only got a little while," said the engineer. "The roof and the cornice is smokin'."

"The cornice will burn and fall down before the wall caves in, I think," the foreman speculated quietly as he peered up through the smoke. "We got to keep the water on the fire as long as we can. The floors an' the walls inside is all wood. We got to keep on playin' water."

"That's right. But not for long. The men have got to be out of this street before the wall collapses."

"Of course. They'll all be crushed if they aren't."

Glass in the third-story window broke. It tinkled brightly as it fell on the sidewalk.

"Look!"

The foreman pointed toward the top floor with a smoke-stained finger. A figure appeared at the window. It was quickly blotted out of sight by a cloud of smoke.

"Help! Help!" The pleading cry came from the open window far above the ground.

"It's too late!" said the foreman. There was hopelessness in his voice.

"Too late," echoed the engineer.

But it was not too late. Not too late to try. It was not too late for Mose. He had heard the cry. And now, with Sykesey, he was bringing a ladder up to the burning building.

The fire had spread across the length of the heavy wooden ornamental cornice that crowned the building at the roof and jutted out over the sidewalk. A thin red line of fire was growing where the cornice met the wall. Like a flowing stream of blood. Slender tongues of flame lapped at the wood and drank it up. It was old and dry. It could not last long.

Mose and Sykesey were hard at work. The top of the ladder sneaked slowly up the wall to the screaming, smoke-shrouded figure in the window. There was another figure there now. Two more.

"Help! Help!" The cries rose above the roar of the fire. They were smothered in the crash of falling

timbers as a lower floor within the brick walls sur-
rendered to the flame.

The ladder was in place. Rising almost straight up
from the center of the street, it touched the fourth-
story window. Flames darted out at the ladder and
curled around the rungs like the grasping tentacles
of a flaming octopus. Mose started up. He half
turned, and shouted over his shoulder: "Play some
water on the ladder."

"It ain't safe," the engineer cried. "We got to get
the men out of the street or the wall will fall on
'em."

The foreman lifted his speaking trumpet. "Back
away!" he shouted.

Mose turned, and began to climb. Didn't he hear?
The foreman ran up closer. "Mose! Mose! Back
away! You'll never make it!" he roared through
the trumpet.

The anguished cries for help increased. Mose
looked up. A cloud of smoke rolled past the window. For a fleeting moment the terrified faces were
clearly visible. No one knew how many there were
peering helplessly from the window, for another
film of smoke blotted out the view.

Mose drew a sharp breath. He shouted down to

the foreman. "Them's kids! Them's kids up there!"

"The wall! You'll never make it!"

"I'm a-goin' to do me dooty!" said Mose firmly.

Sykesey stood at the ladder and held it steady. The water played in the lower windows, on the ladder, on the hot wall, on the ladder again. Up he went. Up. Up. Through the smoke. Up through the hot, stretching, searching fingers of flame.

He reached the top of the ladder. In a moment he would be through the window. There was a cracking sound above. He looked up. Dust and burning embers fell on his face. The cornice was in full flame. Crack! The flaming platform above his head trembled and moved.

Crack! The cornice was slipping. Its supports were all but burned away. In a flaming instant it would fall, and sweep him from the ladder, down to the pavement far below.

The frightened faces were still at the window. The cries for help had faded as help grew near. When the cornice fell and brushed him before it to earth, there would be no help. The cries would come again. Then soon there would be no cries. No cries at all.

More embers fell. There was a deadly groan from

the wavering cornice. It trembled loosely. Mose put his foot against the wall. He bent close to the ladder. His arms straightened out in an impulsive backward thrust. His leg pushed against the wall. The ladder flew back, away from the window sill. It hovered in the air. Straight up it was. Straight up in the air.

On the street below, Sykesey held on and helped as best he could. In the sky above, Mose clung to two long, thin strips of wood, and balanced. A move of a muscle. This way. That way. Back again. The ladder straight up. Like a cane on the end of a circus seal's nose.

And then the cornice fell. Like a flaming meteor it fell, and hit the sidewalk with a deadly crash. Sparks and ashes spread over the street. Sykesey shut his eyes and held on. The men of *Lady Washington Engine Company No. 40* worked the brakes without missing a stroke. The pipe held steady and the water played on the fire.

Mose shifted his weight. The ladder fell back against the window sill where it had rested a moment before. The big fireman stepped inside the trembling, burning building. He looked around the smoke-filled room. "Great sufferin' hooks an' ladders!" he exclaimed.

He had often made rescues from windows, high in flaming buildings. But he had never before been faced with a rescue anything like this one was going to be. One. Two. Three. Four. Five. Could he be seeing double? No. That was right. Five.

There they were before him. Five smoke-be-grimed, tear-stained children, though one was somewhat older than a child.

He must move quickly. The building trembled again as buildings do before a wall collapses. There was not time for five trips down and up that long ladder.

He leaned down. "Are yez scairt?" he asked.

Smoke pressed through the floor and under the door. The boards were hot on his feet. The paint on the smoking wood cracked and curled from the heat. The swelling rush and roar of leaping flames grew steadily.

The children were silent at his question. "Are yez scairt?" he asked again.

A small sniffle came from the little group. "We was scairt. But we ain't no more. Not after what we seen you do," came a thin little voice.

"Then do just like I tell yez. An' do it quick. Like firemen. Line up in a row. The littlest foist."

The crowd below saw Mose come out of the window and stand on the top rung of the ladder. "He was too late," someone said. "The smoke choked 'em."

"Yeah, I s'pose," another said wearily.

"It was a good try, anyways."

"Yeah. A good try."

"Wait! No. Look!"

They looked. They saw a tiny figure in the window. They saw Mose lift the figure out, and tuck it in his left pants pocket.

Then another was lifted out of the window and tucked in the other side pocket.

They saw another figure lifted out of the smoking window. What could he do with that one? They gasped at what they saw. Mose hooked the youngster's clothes over the pointed wings of the brass double eagles on his galluses. A little boy it was. The sturdy india-rubber galluses stretched, and he bounced up and down. He smiled. Bravery begets bravery.

Then another small boy appeared at the window. He was hooked over the outstretched wing tips of the other double eagle. And that boy laughed too as the rubber stretched and he bounced up and down in space.

Mose reached out and took the fifth one under his right arm. She was the one who was somewhat older than a child.

"Look!" Sykesey exploded. "He's got Linda!"

"Linda?"

"Yes! Linda!"

"Linda, the beautiful segar girl?"

"Yes! He's rescued Linda!"

It was true. Mose had rescued Linda, the beautiful segar girl. A favorite of the Bowery B'hoys, and a real Bowery beauty.

He made his way down the long ladder while it swayed and bent like a willow in a gusty wind. The two children hooked over the double eagles bounced and fluttered like dangling orioles' nests at the tips of the willows' branches.

In the street below, a thousand eyes watched the soaring smokey drama. Cricks in necks were forgotten. The fire was leaping far out the window, clawing at the ladder, and where its talons struck, it left growing, glowing gashes of fire. Water from the *White Ghost* played on the ladder, up and down its length. And the smoking rungs became steaming rungs. And the heat of the fire became the heat of steam. The wall trembled again. Every fireman knew it was the final spasm before it crashed to earth.

Steadily, rapidly, big Mose came down. He shouted: "Back away! Back away!"

The company drew back down the narrow street, pushing the onlookers to places of safety. The wall shuddered visibly. It wavered.

Mose's feet touched the ground. Cracks spread over the face of the wall. The ragged gashes widened. Loose bricks tumbled down.

Sykesey reached up for the pretty girl in Mose's arms. "Are yez all right?" he asked.

Linda, the beautiful segar girl, did not speak. There was no need. Her big, beautiful smile told the story. She was safe, and so were her four little brothers and sisters.

A few strides and the big smoke-eater and his human load were beyond the reach of the breaking wall. Sykesey and Linda were at his side.

Then the wall collapsed. Like an avalanche, bricks, plaster, and burning wood crashed down into the street and filled the narrow road.

A volunteer fireman gets no pay and expects no

thanks. But this time it was different. Linda, the beautiful segar girl, gave him her biggest and most beautiful smile. Four small, dirty faces looked up at Mose. From one came the words: "Thank you, Mister Mighty Mose the fireman. Thank you, very much."

Mose looked down at them. "That's all right," he said. "I only done me dooty!"

Fires, Fights, and Frolics

(IN WHICH *is described the Great Fire of 1835; the villainous gangs of Five Points; fights for the honor and protection of the Bowery; Asiatic cholera; friendly fights among firemen; to the fire plug with a barrel; frolics; Firemen's Balls; Chowders; a maiden's broken heart for Mose; torchlight parades; target shoots, and Mose's excellence in that exacting sport; shooting at a bouncing bung-hole; the fireman's life.*

BIG MOSE and the Bowery B'hoys of Little Old New York were always ready for a fight, a fire, or a frolic. Happily, they fought fires. Eagerly, they fought foes. Joyfully, they fought with their friends.

Fireproof construction was unknown, and most of the buildings in those days were ready prey for the fire fiend. The Bowery Theatre burned down three times in a dozen years. The great fire of 1835 brought horror and destruction to much of the city. It was still smoking six months after the December day when it destroyed almost seven hundred buildings. The conflagration raged for two days. The temperature was seventeen degrees below zero. An engine, once started, dared not stop even for a moment. If it did, the water froze in the hose.

A merchant saw the great fire from a roof and described it: "From Maiden Lane to Coenties Slip, and from William Street to the East River, the whole immense area, embracing some 13 acres all in a raging, uncontrollable blaze! ! ! . . . An ocean of fire . . . with roaring, rolling, burning waves, surging onward and upward and spreading certain universal destruction; tottering walls and falling chimneys with black smoke, hissing, clashing sounds on every side. Something like this was the fearful prospect."

Fire engines dashed from Brooklyn. They came from White Plains. They hurried from Newark and Morristown, New Jersey. Volunteers rushed from

Philadelphia, and they dragged their machines for miles across the frozen swamps and hills of New Jersey when the railroad engine broke down.

Soldiers, sailors, and marines joined in the fight. The great fire was at last stopped when the buildings in its path were charged with gunpowder and blown up before the spreading flames could reach them.

Mose, with the *Lady Washington* Company, and with dozens of other engines, and hundreds of firemen, fought the great fire. They fought large fires and small fires, for any one of them could spell destruction. A small fire is only a fire that has not yet grown large.

Mose and the Ghosts, the men who ran with the *White Ghost*, fought the gangs of Five Points. Five Points! Where the public buildings and the stately court houses of Foley Square now stand. Five Points! A villainous, riproaring, violent spot where for years there was a murder every night.

The gangs of Five Points were terror in the streets. The "Dead Rabbits." "Chickchesters." "Pug Uglies." Villainous thugs who ruled the toughest part of town. Some say the toughest part of the world. They ruled it with still other gangs. The "Forty Thieves." "Rock Guards." "Shirt Tails." And the "Black Birds."

They were welcome to stay in Five Points and in their hangouts. These were dives with names that described the character of their occupants: "The Gates of Hell." "Brick Bat Mansion." "Murderer's Alley." "Den of Thieves."

But let them go to the Bowery where hard-working people lived and played and worked, or to near-by Mulberry Street where the *Lady Washington* was housed, and they were sure to meet Big Mose and the Bowery B'hoys. Let them go to Centre Market, and they would meet Mose and the Ghosts. Let them meet the Ghosts, and the gangs of Five Points were sure to retreat in disorder before flailing fists and a rain of flying brickbats.

Centre Market was located where Police Headquarters is today. It was probably established there so the police would be close to the fights. The *Lady Washington* was housed only a block away, in Mulberry Street, near Broome.

"I got nothin' against 'em," Mose would say. "Except they're like colts, mean colts, that ain't been broke to work. They ain't learned that you can't git

somethin' fer nothin'. I feel as much fer a poor feller as anybody livin', but not fer a lazy one. There's
plenty of work in this village fer everybody, if
they're only a mind to look fer it."

So when the gangs of Five Points invaded the
Bowery or Mulberry Street or Centre Market, Mose
would sing out: "Here they come, lookin' fer trouble, an' you can bet high they're goin' to find it!"

And when the brickbats started to fly, Mose would
raise his voice and the gas lights along the Bowery
would flicker and their glass chimneys would rattle.

"Here they come, men. They want a muss, an'
we're right on hand to help out. I'm spilin' fer a
good old knock down and drag out! Then we will
all retire like gentlemen." And with that, he would
wade into the attacking mob.

It was easy for Mose to fight. When his fist landed
on a thug's eye he shouted: "There's a black blinker
fer you!"

But he didn't stop. He went on to another, to put
another eye "in mourning," as he used to say.

If a gangster's fist found Mose's chin, it brought
Mose still another step toward victory. A good
square blow on Mose's granite jaw brought no trouble or pain to Mose. But for his opponent, it was

almost sure to bring a handful of broken knuckles.

You had to fight to be a volunteer fireman in New York in those days. Fight fires. Or fight gangs. You had to like it. The country was growing up. The city was growing. You had to fight to keep up. And Mose loved it. "If it's a muss they want," he would say hopefully, "I'm right on hand."

Or when there was no fight in sight, he would sigh and say: "If I don't have a muss soon, I'll spile." Jim Jeroloman, David Garthwaite, Orange County, Sykesey, and the rest would laugh. What laughter. They could laugh as well as they could fight.

There were other foes for firemen to fight besides fires and the gangs of Five Points. Two of the worst were the plagues of yellow fever and Asiatic cholera. When the people fled north to Greenwich Village and Harlem to escape these, the firemen stayed behind to guard the deserted city. They raised vegetables in the vacant, untraveled streets.

And there were friends to fight, too. The volunteers of other companies. Rivals who wanted to get to the fire first. Every company wanted to be the first to lay water on a fire. Often they would send a man ahead of the engine with a barrel. He clapped the barrel over the fire plug nearest to the fire. And he would release it only to his own machine. When another machine arrived first, what then? Why, a fight. A wild melee between two rival companies. Sometimes more, for the companies arriving still later wanted to put their hose on the disputed fire plug too.

It was easy for rival companies to get into fights over the right of way as they raced to a fire. It was easier still to fight over who did the most and the best at a fire. Of course there were arguments, and arguments produced invective and bitter description: "Do Nothing and Blow Much Engine Company." "Blow and Brag Engine Company." Such words were fighting words and friends found cause to fight. Friends could get in fights too over such vital questions as who pumped the tallest stream over Riley's Pole on a friendly Sunday afternoon.

But fighting was not everything. There were frolics, too. The Firemen's Balls! The first Firemen's Ball was held in the Bowery Theatre in 1829. Everyone was on his good behavior at a Firemen's Ball. Wives and best girls joined in the fun. That was when Mose and Liza Stebbins, his gallus gal, cut a handsome figure.

And the Chowder Nights! What nights! What

chowder! It was real chowder—with tomatoes in it, and garlic and sage and thyme. So it would stick together just right. No soft, weak, creamy clam chowder for Manhattan's firemen. There were clams in it too. Lots of them. No clam had a greater aspiration than to end up in the volunteer firemen's Manhattan clam chowder! Yes, they put clams in. Real clams. And there they stayed, happy as a clam, as the saying goes.

They would start off with oysters. Three dozen for Mose. Then there would be pork and beans, and Mose would shout: "Gimme a plate of pork and beans. Go heavy on the pork, an' don't stop to count the beans!"

And Jim Jeroloman would roar with laughter. And the gold earrings would toss back and forth like fire bells swinging in the air and singing out their alarm.

And Sykesey would laugh too. Laugh with pride, and cry: "That Mose! Vot a man! Twice as large as life, an' t'ree times as nachural!"

Then they would fall to, and eat chowder, and pork and beans. For dessert there would be a jig, a dance, a song, and more laughter.

Linda, the beautiful segar girl, would look at Mose. She would recall the time he rescued her from what seemed to be certain death in a burning building, and she would sigh, and she would whisper to herself: "Ah, Mose. A true specimen of one of the B'hoys!"

She would recall still another scene when Mose had rescued a little child, and the speech when Mose was cited for bravery, when the child's father had said: "I can never own a prouder title than the friend of honest industry and lion-hearted courage."

She recalled Mose's modest reply. "Shucks. It ain't nothin'. I run with the masheen, don't I? I only done me dooty. I love that enjine. I love her better than I do me dinner. She t'rows a t'ree-inch stream. The purtiest in town. When folks is in a boinin' buildin', they usually needs rescuin'. An' it seems like I just got to rescue 'em."

Linda, the beautiful segar girl, recalled these things. But she knew there was no hope for her. Not with Mose. Liza Stebbins was Mose's gallus gal, and Linda had heard Mose himself say: "I'll be blowed if Lize ain't slap up. She's a prize lamb. As gallus a piece of calico as any around. Mebbe I'll git slung to her one of these days."

But the frolics. Firemen's Balls and Chowders. Parades. Parades at every celebration. Daylight parades. Torchlight parades. Thrilling torchlight parades. The most thrilling and impressive sight the city had to offer. With countless flaming torches lighting the city streets. Tall shadows looming and swaying on the faces of the tall buildings. And countless marching feet, pulsing thunder on the cobblestones. Thunder to the rhythm of blaring bands of music.

There were target shoots when the Lady Washington Guards shouldered their guns and marched away for a day in the country, far away from their island city. A day in friendly, green Hoboken. Or in a quiet, clean spot on the edge of Gowanus Creek. Or on pretty Newtown Creek near the neat little village of Williamsburg. Or in the uncluttered, open spaces of Flushing.

At the target shoots the best marksman could win prizes. Half a hog. A quarter of beef. A fat goose. Welcome prizes for a man with a real, man-sized appetite.

Mose could use a gun as well as he could use a pipe, a hose, or a hook. He could light a match by grazing its head with a bullet at sixty paces. With the next shot, he could snuff out the flame.

Everyone remembered the time they were shooting at the bung-hole in a barrel. The barrel toppled over and started to roll down the long hill toward Flushing Bay. It bumped and bounced over the rocks as it rolled. Mose shot at it six times before it reached the bottom and stopped rolling. He won the prize that time. Every shot hit its mark, and went into the bouncing bung-hole.

There were quiet times, too. Times when there were neither fights nor frolics. Sunday afternoons at the engine house. Evenings, when the machine was cleaned, the hose repaired, and the equipment checked.

They stood around and talked. They talked about fires that had been, and were to be. They talked about the times they had stood shoulder to shoulder in the smoke and heat and flames of burning rooms. About the leakage from the nozzle and how the river water ran down their arms and into their boots. And about the time Mose stood so long at a fire with a hose in his hands that fish grew to full size in his boots. About the time the wind changed and the water blew back on them and they got as wet as if they had been under water an hour.

They talked solemnly about the time the Methodist Book Concern burned. The next day in Flushing where the high wind had blown it, a burned and charred fragment of a page from the Bible had been found. On it, untouched by flame, were these words from the eleventh verse, the sixty-fourth chapter of Isaiah: "Our holy and our beautiful house, where our fathers praised thee, is burned up with fire; and all our pleasant things are laid waste."

They talked about Mose. About the time he stretched out between windows, across a narrow alley. Three stories up. And the volunteers, using him as a human bridge, rescued twenty people from the clutch of fire.

There were jokes. The one about the man who struck a match to see if the oil can was full. It was. That man made a brand new skylight then and there. And he wasn't a carpenter either. Another man did the same thing. He floated to heaven in pieces. That's what they said. A fireman could always laugh at that.

Some people saw them in these happy, gossipy, friendly moments, and said they were loafers. But the volunteers loafed only on Sunday. The other days of the week they were ship builders, iron workers, brass founders, printers, butchers, mechanics, merchants, bankers. They came from every occupation

and every walk of life. They had one thing in common. They were willing to face danger to help their neighbors.

Fire fighting was excitement and adventure. It was also a civic duty. It was civic co-operation. It was helping others. It was protecting the weak. While other men were leaving the city for the perils of the new wild West with its Indians, buffalo, longhorns, and gold, the volunteers found danger and duty at home, with fire.

Many mayors of New York had run with the machines. George Washington himself had been a fireman. There was something in the blood that made the smoke-eaters want to fight fires. There was something about a "wet coat" that made them eager to endanger their own lives to save the lives of others. For the men who had "held a rope" or "carried a pipe," and who had the "smell of hose leather on their hands," there was no getting away from it.

They had a pride, the volunteer firemen did. And it was pride well justified, for it came from the knowledge of a good job well done.

Mighty Mose

(IN WHICH *several of Mose's heroic fire-fighting adventures are related; an explosion and a flight through space; a swim and a bit of jumping; a grievous fall; a burning roof, a life endangered, and a miraculous escape from death.*

T H E bad fires were usually at night and in the winter time. It was at night that fires grew large before they were discovered. It was in the winter time that tame fires in the fireplaces became angered by faulty chimneys and went mad, and the friendly fires in lamps and candles became wild when touched by accident or carelessness.

123

There were incendiary fires, with the arsonist's criminal touch. Evil creating evil. And there were fires of innocence, thoughtlessness, or disobedience. Children playing with matches, releasing a flood of destruction and cruelty at the end of a little stick.

Ten, even twenty times a night, the bells cried out for the help of the New York Volunteer Fire Department. One or two engines for a small fire. Two- or three-dozen engines for a large fire, and a score of hook-and-ladder and hydrant companies too. Many times every fireman and every machine was called to save the city from flames.

There is always danger with every fire. Mose ran to more fires than anyone else. Little wonder he had more adventures than anyone else.

There was the time he was on the roof of a burning building. There was gunpowder inside. No one knew that. Not at first. But when the fire reached the gunpowder, everyone south of Fulton Street and west of Broadway knew it. Knew it very well indeed.

The explosion shook Manhattan's solid rock foundation. The walls of the burning building flew apart in a shower of countless splinters. The roof, with Mose on it, shot up in the air.

When the explosive force spent itself, the roof

began to turn on its side to complete its trip in a crashing dive to earth. The sound of the explosion faded away in the folds of its own echoes. The sounds of the city streets could not reach such a height. The big fireman was alone on the flying roof in the silence of the sky.

The flat roof hovered in space for a brief moment. Mose could hear the mournful, mewing cry of the Hudson River gulls as they soared on the capricious air currents around him.

He began to fall, still clinging to the free-flying roof. The wind whistled past his soap locks as the downward speed of the roof increased, rushing to the earth, and oblivion. The gulls screamed louder. To many men their lonesome cry would have been a dirge of death.

But not to Mose. He shifted his weight. The roof leveled off. Its speed decreased. An upward thrust of air caught it from below, and like a giant kite without a tail it sailed up the line of the hill toward Broadway. Twice around Trinity Church steeple it soared. Once around St. Paul's as it headed north, Mose shifting his position to guide his flying platform. It twitched and fluttered like an eagle with the hiccups.

The gulls screamed, and soared in smaller circles. When the upward air currents failed them, they could flap their wings and regain their height. But Mose, on his flying roof top, could supply no more power. The first explosive charge of gunpowder was gone. There was no more power.

His luck had carried him far enough. The updraft melted away. His impromptu craft made a long, sloping dive for the pleasant shore of Hoboken, across the river. It hit the river at a gentle angle, and skipped along a few times like a flat stone thrown on the surface of quiet water.

The last skip brought the roof, with Mose still on it, to the Jersey shore. It had all happened quickly. As quick as the flight of a bird. He stood on the soft green sod of Hoboken, in the shade of friendly trees. He looked back across the river. Smoke was still pushing up. There was still a fire. Mose knew he should be there. Duty called. A dive, and he was in the Hudson. Two strokes and he was across.

Mose could swim across the Hudson in two strokes. He could swim around Manhattan in six strokes. With favorable tides and friendly winds he could make it in five.

Swimming is a good way to get across a river.

128

Especially one as wide as the Hudson. But Mose had a better way to get across the East River to Brooklyn. He jumped across. At least, that's what people said.

It may have seemed that he jumped across. But that, strictly speaking, is not true. It was really very simple. He tightened his galluses. The rubber stretched as tight as a miser's purse strings and pulled his pants up hard. Naturally, when his pants were pulled up, Mose, being in them, was pulled up too. Jumping was obviously easy. It was possible for him to get up in the air a considerable distance before the law of gravity took hold and kept him from flying off into outer space.

The upward pull from his galluses gave him an unusual buoyancy, and a consequent reputation as a jumper, which, in all honesty, he did not entirely merit.

It is not difficult to stretch an unusual circumstance like this into out-and-out untruths. As the years have passed and the stories have been told and retold, there has been an unfortunate tendency to exaggerate. It should always be remembered, that while Mose was a great jumper, he could never have jumped across the East River. That is, not without the very real help of his very tight suspenders, their upward pull, and, naturally, their resilience. The resilience is important, for it permitted him to come back to earth once he got under way through space. Few will disagree that Mose had one of the quickest and best ways ever devised to get to Brooklyn. Imaginative people talked and dreamed about a bridge to Brooklyn. But such fanciful speculation was frowned upon by sober, realistic, sensible folk. It was clear there could never be a bridge to Brooklyn.

If his galluses were not unusually tight, gravity acted upon Mose much like it acts on other people. And with similar results. Take for example the time he was on the roof of a six-story building. There was no explosion that time to take him flying off to New Jersey and the soft green shade of Hoboken. Nor were his suspenders tight enough at the time to hold him up.

He was on the roof fighting a fire. The smoke was so thick he had to cut through it with an axe. He couldn't see where he was going. It is said that when the smoke was thick he pulled his head down into his neck, like a turtle.

He probably did something like that, because in all his fire fighting he was never overcome by smoke poisoning, and he could stay in the thickest, foulest smoke long after other firemen fell. That's why they often called him Smokey Mose.

Maybe that's what he did. That day on the roof. Pulled in his neck. At any rate, he didn't see where the edge of the roof was. And he walked right off the six-story building. That was one time Mose got hurt. Sprained his right ankle. Everyone thought he would be laid up for a couple of weeks. But he used an oak wagon-tongue for a cane. It worked all right, too. He never missed a fire.

After that he always kept a sharp lookout when he was on a roof. He wasn't going to come down the short way again if he could help it. As luck would have it, it wasn't long after that when he found himself on a roof again. A burning roof. That wasn't surprising because Mose fought so many fires that he spent more time on burning roofs than he did in bed.

It was one of those occasions when speed is necessary. The building was going to fall. It was trembling and shuddering, the way a building always does when it is in its death throes.

There was no ladder on the roof. There wasn't time to put one up. Mose peered down through the smoke and flame. "Sykesey!" he shouted.

Sykesey was in the street. Water was playing through the broken windows. He looked up.

"Put six men on the pipe!" Mose commanded.

Six men sprang to the pipe. They didn't know why. The building was past help. But Mose said to do it, so they did.

"All hands at the brakes!" the big smoke-eater ordered from his smokey height. The Ghosts crowded up to the brakes.

"Now, pump away. Work hard!" Mose shouted. Muscles strained against the brakes. Water pushed into the leader. The hose stiffened.

"Play the water here!" said Mose. "Toward me!" The long, hard stream of water left its idle playing in the windows. It stretched up to the roof and the solitary figure standing there, calm in the face of danger. No one doubted that Mose knew what he was doing. He had a purpose. But no one yet knew what the purpose was.

They saw Mose reach out and touch the stream as it shot past him. It was a hard, cold stream. Like a shaft of steel. At his next move, they understood. They bent to the brakes. They could not stop or falter now.

The *White Ghost* absorbed their strength. And

through the brakes and condensers and pistons their strength turned into a long, hard, slender stream of water.

The six men at the pipe held it straight and firm. They struggled against the stress and strain that sought to tear it from their hands. For Mose had left the building. And now he was clinging to the slender, hard-packed stream of water. Quickly he slid down it until his feet struck the brass pipe held by six surprised and straining men. He let go, and dropped the last few feet to safety.

The company quickly withdrew. The building shuddered, wavered a moment, and then crunched down into the empty street. Clouds of dust and the hollow rumble of a dying building beat against the walls that had been saved from the destroying touch of fire.

There was only one casualty. That was Mose. But a slight casualty. Got some slivers in his hands as he slid down.

Icicles, Firecicles, and the Big Blow

*[IN WHICH *there is told a tale of a cold night, a fire, and the strange, but scarcely breathless way Mose conquered it; Mose's pranks; danger in the turbulent tides of Hell Gate at the entrance to Long Island Sound; Mose to the rescue.*

ONCE, the alarm bells rang and Mose was the only fireman in the city who reached the fire. That was the year of the big rain. Some folks say it was the longest, hardest, and wettest rain since Noah's time. The other men couldn't get to the engine house. Not a single one. Mose was the only one who made it. He got to the engine house. And he got to the fire. Pulled the *White Ghost* all alone that time. It was raining so hard he had to swim every inch of the way.

Another time, Mose put a fire out by himself. Well, maybe he didn't put it out. Technically, anyway. But he disposed of it.

It was a big fire. Several companies answered the alarm. In the beginning, the street was filled with a swirl of curling hoses, struggling men, and thumping machines. But in the end, Mose put the fire out alone.

It was cold that night. Colder than an eskimo's nose. One by one, the men from the other companies had stopped to get warm. Their engines froze. When an engine stopped pumping, even for a moment, the water froze in the pumps. Then that engine was out of action.

Only the *White Ghost* remained at work. She never missed a stroke. But it was so cold, the water, pumped from the Hudson, began to thicken. Someone rolled a barrel of brandy out of the burning building. Mose poured some of it into the pumps to keep them from freezing. One of the shivering men said: "If brandy keeps the pumps thawed out, it ought to keep the men thawed out, too."

Mose heard him. "I'll show you how a good fireman uses brandy when he's fightin' fire," he said. He took a dipperful, and dumped it into his boots.

"Brandy in the pumps keep them from freezin'. Brandy in boots keeps a fireman's feet from freezin'. No man does any drinkin' on the job as long as he's in this company." He squished his toes through the liquid in his boots. "It's colder than the glare of a killer polar bear," he said. "But it don't freeze."

The men stayed at the brakes. The stream of water, once light and quick flowing, had thickened with the cold until it was like molasses. Like molasses in January, which is understandable, because it was a January night.

And soon the molasses-like stream began to leave the pipe in an even harder and tougher stream. Like a wet, cold rope. It was really cold that night.

The water got through the suction pipe and through the air chamber. There, the brandy had its effect and kept it from freezing. But there was no protection from the cold in the long stretch of hose. It froze. Long icicles shot out from the nozzle. They cracked and popped as they shot out and broke off.

Icicles sped through the air. An endless barrage of silver arrows. But arrows are not proper weapons for fighting fires. Not even arrows of ice.

For a moment it seemed that the heroic efforts of the *Lady Washington Engine Company No. 40* were doomed to failure. It would be the first time the company had ever failed to put out a fire. All the other engines were out of commission. That being the case, it would also be the first time New York was ever burned to the ground.

The men worked hard. Beads of sweat formed. They trickled to the tips of chins and noses. There they dangled for a cold moment and fell, freezing into icy marbles that made cold music as they bounced against the icy cobblestones and danced away down the hill.

The flames suddenly stopped flickering off into nothingness as they darted skyward. Mose couldn't understand it. Something seemed to catch them before the last flicker. Caught them and held them in being.

Solid flame? It didn't seem possible. The tips of the flames broke off and fell tinkling to the pavement with the icicles from the hose. It took Mose a few moments to realize what was happening.

Then he knew what it was. The fire was freezing too. Not at the base of the blaze. There, it was too hot to freeze. But the tips of the flame. The fire climbed and danced up in the freezing air and there fell prey to the cold. It froze. Firecicles.

Mose quickly saw the hidden danger. The frozen flames would burst out into raw fire when they thawed out. The fire couldn't possibly be put out that night. Probably not until the spring thaw came. That would never do, and something had to be done. It was no good wasting time with a fire like that. Not on such a night. There was no telling what would happen next. It was best to take no chances.

As long as something had to be done, Mose did it! He took a deep breath. A good, deep one. He blew against the flame. Hard! And he blew the fire out.

He kicked the firecicles and the icicles off the sidewalk and the porch where they had fallen. He nudged them with his foot into a pile of snow at the curb.

The fire was out. The hot part, anyway. The frozen part would be put out when the spring thaw came. Obviously when the firecicles thawed, the icicles and the snow would thaw too, and would quench whatever flames might develop. The company, stiff with cold, and somewhat shocked with surprise, made its way back to the engine house.

It should not have surprised the Ghosts too much when Mose blew the fire out. He had a voice like a foghorn, so it stands to reason that he could blow hard. They had seen him blow before. There was the time, for instance, down at the foot of Broad Street. There was another fire. The ships in the slip seemed doomed. The sailors on board, in a desperate effort to escape, had set the sails. But there was no wind. The poison tongues of the growing flames would soon touch the canvas.

Mose rushed around to the leeward side. He got as close as he could, and blew! The sails filled. He blew again, and the ships edged away from the shore. Another long steady blow and they moved out into the bay. Safe from the fire.

Mose found amusement in blowing ships back to the ocean as they tried to make their way to the slips that lined the shore. Sometimes at night he would go to Bowling Green and blow against the ships at anchor in the Upper Bay. They would respond to the force of his breath and drag their anchors down through the Narrows and into the Lower Bay. He liked to be at the slip when the ship made port the next day, and listen to the captain describe the force of the current and the wind that moved his ship in the night.

Mose really could blow all right. The Ghosts remembered another time. They were on their way to a shooting match on the shore of Flushing Bay. They were in a small sailing boat. When they were in the turbulent currents of Hell Gate, the wind failed. Their ship went out of control. It was swept rapidly along by the strong tide toward the rocky mainland shore. Disaster seemed sure. Suddenly the sails filled. The bow turned mysteriously away from the rocks. The ship plowed against the current through the rough water. A comforting white wake turned up at the stern. But there was no wind on deck.

"Vot hoppen?" asked Sykesey.

"Don't know," Jim Jeroloman replied.

"There ain't no vind."

"But the sails is full. There is plenty of wind up there even if there ain't none blowin' down here," said Jim, as his eyes scanned the swelling sails above.

"I got a feelin' I should git scairt," said Sykesey.

"Me too."

The still, heavy heat of the summer day was oppressive. But the sails stretched out full. It was strange. Unreal.

Then suddenly it all became very real, and quite simple. It was Mose. He was standing at the stern. He was facing the sails and he seemed to be whistling. He was puckered up like he might be whistling. But there was no whistle. No sound.

He was blowing. Blowing long, steady, low blows into the sails. His breath tore through the ropes and against the canvas. And the sails stretched out as tight as an Indian war drum. The full, taut sails carried the ship through the strong, treacherous waters of Hell Gate, into the smooth expanse of Flushing Bay.

Strangely enough, history does not record that Mose was ever called a blowhard.

The Parade

❨ IN WHICH *is an account of the first fireman's parade and the place of* Lady Washington Engine No. 40 *in that magnificent spectacle; shining machines; the unusual brightness of the* White Ghost; *how she responded to the sunlight; how she saved the day; the origin of the Great White Way.*

WHAT a parade it was! The one when the volunteers first marched. Every engine company, every hose company, every hydrant company, and every hook-and-ladder company, for the first time, shined up and came out for the march up Broadway.

That was July 4, 1824. That was the day of the

greatest parade. Greater even than when the Erie Canal was opened the next year.

Between every company of volunteer firemen was a marching group and a band of music. Not a silent minute. Not a slow or quiet instant. That was a real parade! No long stretches of nothing or not much of anything. No weak and wavering lines of tired citizens in ordinary clothes. But marchers! In uniforms! Long, straight rows of soldiers, sailors, and marines. Bands of music. Marching guards. And the Volunteer Fire Department! Straight and strong! Company after company!

Equipment clean and sparkling. Shining with paint and elbow grease. Marching up the street that would one day be the longest street in the world. Broadway!

There was one engine that was brighter than all the others. *Lady Washington Engine No. 40!* Everything was spit and polish, as they say. The men had toiled over their uniforms and the machine. The brass double eagles on their galluses were as bright as Christmas-tree ornaments. Buttons glistened like joyful tears of laughter.

The white paint of the *White Ghost* was like the snow that fell way out in the country where the snow falls clean and white. Up near the little village of Harlem, for example, seven miles away from the smoke and soot of the city. And the gold on her sides—and the brass air chamber— It was Mose himself who had shined the gold and the brass. And how he had worked!

The gold and the brass shone like—like—like—the sun! That was it. Like the sun. People along the street tried to look at her when she passed. They squinted and blinked their eyes. They turned their heads away a little as the *White Ghost* rolled by. Like people do when they try to look at the sun.

And as the engine moved over the cobblestones the brass air chamber trembled with the roughness of the street. And the light of the sun danced between the sun in the sky and the brilliant, shining dome of the machine. It flashed clean and bright, like lightning in a spring shower. And it darted to the twinkling hub caps. It trembled on the sparkling bolts and ornaments, and it shimmered on the golden trim.

The parade went on and on. The bands of music played. The machines rumbled proudly behind straight, clean lines of volunteers.

The afternoon passed. A glorious afternoon, filled

with color and music and form. The sun went down. But night and darkness did not come. The people wondered why. Then they looked at the *Lady Washington*, and they knew.

Some of the sun was caught in her polished brass and her shining gold and in her glistening, gleaming white. And it could not get away. It shone like what it was. Sunlight. The engine gave off light after the sun went down.

And some of the sun was caught in the American double eagles on Mose's galluses. They gleamed and glistened as if they had somehow caught the rays of Manhattan's sun in their sharp, hooked beaks. They glittered and shimmered as if they had managed to open their brass talons and clutch a sparkling bundle of sunbeams in their metal claws.

Sykesey's double eagles, and those snapped on the galluses of the rest of the company, were shining, too. Fewer rays in smaller beaks. Fewer sunbeams in smaller talons. But still, they sparkled like small pieces of the sun. Every one of them.

And when the men marched, their black leather shoes caught the rays of the truant sunlight from brass buttons, buckles, and double-eagle gallus clasps. From whirling hub caps, flashing gold trim,

and the glowing brass air chamber. Highlights on the moving leather shimmered like a convention of excited glowworms. Flashed and danced like a picnic of fireflies. Sang like the flame of stars reflected from a million waves on the broad expanse of the Hudson.

The Grand Marshal came running toward the gleaming *Lady Washington Engine No. 40.* "Mose. Mose," he called.

Mose heard him. "Company, halt!" he ordered. The men paused in their march. Their moving feet marked time to the blare of trombones, the shrill blast of cornets, the oomph-pa of the bass horns, the boom of the drums, and the trill of the piccolos. The band of music played on.

"Mose," shouted the Grand Marshal as he came puffing up to the big fireman. He squinted his eyes when his gaze crossed the double eagles flashing on the big volunteer's red-shirted chest.

Mose turned toward the Grand Marshal. Light glistened on the sweeping curve of his soap lock. It flashed fire like the tail of Halley's Comet swooping through the black of the night sky.

"It's growing dark back at the reviewing stand," the Grand Marshal exclaimed.

150

"Can't understand that," Mose replied, shouting above the blare of the bands of music. "It ain't dark here."

"No, it ain't," said the Grand Marshal. "And it won't be back there, either, if you will do something for me."

"What?" Mose asked.

"Just come back there with your engine and your men."

"But we're a-marchin' in the pee-rade. We started marchin', an' I always likes to finish what I starts."

"Then go ahead and finish it. After that, bring your engine back to the reviewing stand," the Grand Marshal replied. "If you don't," he added, "we will have to call the parade off on account of darkness. But your machine is shining so bright there is daylight all around it. If you bring it back there like I ask, you'll save the day."

"We'll do it," said Mose. "Just as soon as we finish the pee-rade, we'll bring the masheen to the reviewin' stand."

"Thanks a lot," said the Grand Marshal. "You'll make this parade a great success if you do."

"Us volunteer firemen always do our dooty at a fire," said Mose. "We'll soitenly do the best we can fer a pee-rade. *Enjine No. 40* is soitenly a great masheen. It will be just another time that *Enjine No. 40* will save the day."

So Mose took the *White Ghost* with its captured sunlight back to the reviewing stand. And there it remained, with all the company stretched out in a long line up and down Broadway.

The *White Ghost* stood bright and light in front of the reviewing stand. The rest of the volunteer companies and the bands of music marched past in the light of the captured sunshine.

People cheered and they called Broadway the Great White Way. And ever since, the folks who live in New York have been trying to make it as bright as it was the night *Lady Washington Engine No. 40* caught and held the light of the sun.

It was two weeks before all the truant sunlight left the gold and brass of the *White Ghost* and went back to the sun where it belonged.

An Incident in Chatham Square

[IN WHICH is told how Mose was changed by success; a race on a sunny Sunday afternoon; a memorable fight and a great defeat; a washing; the effect on Mose; "The bigger they are, the harder they fall"; "You can't win all the time"; a new life and new ambitions; a great day; farewell to a true hero.

MOSE won all the time, whether at frolics, fights, or fires. He won at everything. He was strong and brave and quick and clever. He won so much of the time that he quite forgot the sailor and St. Paul's burning steeple of his childhood. And he quite forgot the words of wisdom the sailor spoke.

153

Once he fought fires to help his city and his neighbors. Once he fought fires for the love of the fight. But no more. Now he thought more of the praise that would come to him.

The members of the company, his own company, were loyal to him. But mingled with the cheers that rose from the sidewalks of New York there were jeers, though Mose heard only the praise.

He was still admired, still praised, and it pleased him. But some people saw the change come over Mose. Once there had been only agreement when mention was made of his great size. But now there was often a cynical, even hopeful response. "Yes. He is big. But the bigger they are, the harder they fall."

There was no doubt about it. He was still the best fireman in the city. The only trouble was, he knew it. And he didn't let himself or anyone else forget it.

He rescued a woman and her baby from a burning roof. The ladder was too short. He put eight barrels on top of a packing case and a ladder on top of that wavering, fragile base. No one else could have done it. No one else would have thought of it and dared it.

He carried burning gunpowder out of a flaming

building. He put it down a block away from the crowd. He did it so quickly that he was halfway back to the fire before the glowing gunpowder exploded.

Too bad that he didn't remember that you can't win all the time.

It happened on a sunny Sunday afternoon. The fire was away downtown, on South Street. There was no need for the *White Ghost* to go, nor was there need for the *Red Rover,* nor for the *Old Turk.*

Most of all, there was no need for the *Old Maid* to go.

But it was a beautiful day. The engine houses were open. The engines had been cleaned and shined. The volunteers, the voluntary aids, and the fire buffs were standing around the engines and on street corners, talking, joking, boasting. Mose was boasting. Most of all, Mose was boasting.

Distant fire bells sounded. They shouldn't have gone. None of them. But it was the sort of day they ran the engines just for the fun of it. A little excitement is better than none. A little fire needs to be put out even though it is away down on South Street, and even though there are engines much, much closer.

The Ghosts, the Bloods, the Fly-by-Nights, the Rovers, the Turks, and the Dock Rats. They were all in the streets that fine summer day. So away the engines went! Down the streets they raced! No one lined them up. No one fired a starting gun. There was no tape across the way at the end. But it was a race anyway.

The fire was out when they got there. They started back by different streets. In front of City Hall they came together again. On Park Row. Chatham Street, it was called then.

The *White Ghost* and the *Old Maid* were on the same street. They were going in the same direction. This was a race, and everybody knew it. They started even. How would they finish?

Mose was leading the *White Ghost*. Big Henry was at the head of the *Old Maid's* drag rope. Five hundred Bloods and Fly-by-Nights were running on the right side of the street. Several hundred Ghosts were running on the left. The *Red Rover* and the *Old Turk* followed with a horde of Rovers and Turks in their wake.

Big Henry and Mighty Mose were abreast. Jim Jeroloman was at the wheel rope. A giant of a man was opposite him, running with the Dock Rats.

They raced down the hill past the edge of Five Points. They started up the hill toward Chatham Square and the Bowery. Every muscle strained. The Dock Rats remembered how the *Old Maid* had been washed by the *White Ghost* and pumped dry by the *Red Rover*. They remembered that Mose had spoiled their long history of victory. The Bloods and the Fly-by-Nights running alongside their cherished *Old Maid* remembered, too. It wouldn't happen again. Not if they could help it.

The *Lady Washington* Company remembered too. So did the Ghosts who ran beside them. They had beaten the *Old Maid* once before. They could do it again. Didn't they have the best engine in town? Didn't they have Mighty Mose?

What a race! Neither company could get ahead. Neither gained an inch on the other. The sidewalks were filled with Sunday afternoon strollers. They crowded toward the curb. They moved into the street the better to see the men and machines that were speeding toward them.

Where Chatham Square narrowed into the Bowery, the road was almost filled with the excited crowd. There was not enough room for two racing machines abreast.

157

But the race could end. The *White Ghost* could turn away, down Mulberry Street, to its engine house. They could call it a tie.

No. Not the *White Ghost*. Not the cocky *White Ghost*. Not as long as Big Mose was at the head. There could be no tie. There must be victory. Nothing else would do for Mose!

The engines flew up the hill. The crowds forced the machines closer together. Big Mose and Big Henry were close now. Running side by side.

The speeding machines crossed Chatham Square. They approached the Bowery. Crowds pressed in on each side.

There was no longer room for two machines. The hub caps brushed together with an angry groan. They edged away only to draw together again with a crash! There was an anguished shriek as metal tires grated across the cobbles, kicking up a shower of sparks and dust. The opposing companies jerked to a confused halt!

There were angry cries. Warnings. Quick words. Harsh words. A push here. A shove there. An elbow raised. A fist clenched. A hat knocked off. A coat torn.

Tempers flared. The hot blood of quick fighters

was in the square. The bad blood of rival companies was there. Hot blood and bad blood boiled! In a flash, a race became a fight!

Mose and Big Henry faced each other. A tumult of tangling Ghosts, Bloods, and Fly-by-Nights tumbled about them. Scuffling feet, flailing fists, grunts and shouts, thuds and curses violated the sunny, summer Sunday afternoon!

Mose felt no fear. Why should he? Hadn't he been winning all the time? Too bad he didn't remember.

"As for you," he shouted at Henry, "don't waste me time. I'm spilin' for a muss. When me hand falls on you, yez can be sure it will leave a mark!"

"Quit the chin music an' let it fall," was the reply.

"Don't twiddle your tongue so much. I aim to give yez me number one wallop," Mose cried.

Most men trembled at such a threat from such a man. But Big Henry was not disturbed. "Better take real good aim then, because you got a wallop like a wisp of smoke, an' it don't scare me none," he said.

"Sure, be careful yez don't git your eyes full of smoke then," Mose shouted.

"I'll be doin' some punchin' myself."

"Yez couldn't punch your way out of a paper bag with a fire axe in one hand an' a spannin' iron in the

159

other." Mose punctuated this last verbal onslaught with a wide swing with his fist. His blow connected with Henry's jaw. Henry returned a right to the ribs, and the fight was on.

They clinched. They were down. Rolling on the cobblestones. They were up. They traded blow for blow. There were no rules. Both hands and both feet worked where they could do the most damage. Knees and elbows went to work. All holds were used. Heel stomping. Eye gouging too. Anything.

A thousand other men and boys were in the fray. Ghosts and Rovers and Turks found Bloods, Dock Rats, and Fly-by-Nights to fight! Chatham Square, from Mulberry Street to the Bowery, was a mad confusion of fighting, struggling men. In the center of the turmoil were Mose and Henry, and Jim Jero-loman and his giant opponent.

Eyes in mourning. Mice. Brown blinkers. Call them what you will. Black eyes were being made on every hand, with every fist.

Hundreds of fist fights at once. Men were down and men were out. But the fight went on. Jim Jero-loman fell beneath the blows of the giant who opposed him. That was tragic. The Ghosts and their friends knew it at once. But Mose was still fighting. And Mose, Big Mose, Mighty Mose, Smokey Mose the smoke-eater, was still with them. They fought on!

Mose and Henry clinched again. Once more they crashed down on the rocky street. They landed with a thud that shook the walls of the Bowery Theatre. Mose was on top! The fight was as good as over now. He could win. But that wasn't enough for Mose. He wanted to humiliate his opponent.

He knew the way. He knew just how to do it. He spread a big hand over Henry's face. His flat palm pushed his victim's lip up. The teeth were exposed in what seemed to be a malevolent snarl. His big thumb and forefinger went into Henry's mouth. They clamped on a front tooth. Mose jerked, and Henry's tooth came out!

Henry sensed the epic misfortune that had fallen on him. He had lost a tooth. But it had not been knocked out in a straightforward blow with a clenched fist. It had not even been decently knocked out with a flying brickbat. It had been pulled out! The Bowery would rock with laughter. Such a thing would never be forgotten.

161

It could never be left unavenged. Big Henry made a superhuman effort. He gave a violent thrust. Mose responded to the force. He slipped backward. A mean little thug from Five Points slipped up behind Mose. He was cross-eyed and he had a harelip. He also had a monkey wrench in his hand. As Mose fell back the thug raised the monkey wrench and brought it down on Mose's head with deadly force. Mose staggered under the blow. Henry was up. As Mose wavered from side to side, Henry let him have it. A long, hard uppercut that came from the pavement!

It lifted Mose three feet off the ground. He fell straight out! Flat as a policeman's foot. He did not move.

Mose was stretched out, as cold as a side of beef. The Ghosts, the Rovers, and the Turks knew at once. The incredible, the impossible had happened. They were alone. Their champion was gone! He was down and out! It was all over! They retreated in wild disorder!

The next day they found the *White Ghost*. She was in a gutter. In the alley next to the *Old Maid*'s engine house. She was upside down in a puddle of muddy water. She was the picture of abject defeat. The *White Ghost* had been washed by the *Old Maid*.

Her sparkling white and her shining gold had been washed off. She was blotched and scarred. Her soaked and darkened wood ached beneath rough scabs of mud. Beauty and strength and pride lay wounded in a gutter.

They waited until it was dark to haul her home through the somber streets. They waited until the quiet dead of night, so they would be safe from the hurt of laughter, and the pain of jokes and jeers.

The following day the defeated company straggled to the engine house. Despair and defeat bore down heavily on the group. When Mose arrived he answered their looks with words.

"I got this all figgered out," he said. "We got whipped in a fight. I got whipped in a fight. I sure did!" He grinned wryly as he rubbed his head.

"Whether it was a fair fight or not don't make no difference now. My head will get well. The *White Ghost* will get painted up. She'll be shinin' an' fightin' again. We all ought to keep fightin' too. Fightin' fires, that is!"

He looked intently at the men. I'll fight 'em anyway. I learned my lesson. I ought to say I learned it over again, because I learned it once before, when I was a little shaver."

"What's that? What lesson?" Sykesey asked.

"You can't win all the time." Mose paused. "A sailor told me that once, a long time ago. But I sort of forgot."

"I ain't as big as you," Sykesey said. "I can't rightly expect to win very much of the time. Almost everyone is big enough to whip me."

"Size ain't so much, because you really don't lose if you keep on fightin'. Keep on goin'," said Mose. "'Course I'm big. But I got a little too big for me britches. What they say is true. The bigger they are, the harder they fall. I fell real hard. Guess the whole company did. But, if you wound easy you got to heal quick. It ain't never too late to get up an' get started again. You got to keep lookin' up. When you're on top it ain't easy to look up. But when you're flat on your back like I was there in Chatham Square, it's easy. All you got to do is open your eyes."

Mose was speaking easily. His black eye and his skinned cheek bone did not seem to bother him. He continued. "Engine Company Number 15 ain't no gang from Five Points. It's a real good engine company, an' it's got a lot of real good firemen in it. An' Big Henry. He ain't no gangster. He's a volunteer fireman! Same as we are. I'm agoin' to find him an' fix things up."

He strode down Grand Street to the Bowery. He turned and walked up the famous thoroughfare. His company followed. He found Big Henry at the corner of Chatham Square where the two giants had so recently been locked in battle. A crowd had gathered at the sight of Mose and the Ghosts striding toward the Dock Rats. The air was heavy with emotion. Would the two rival volunteers continue the struggle? If they did, the conflict would spread to their companies, and to all other companies. Fires would go unchecked while firemen fought in the streets.

Mose walked up to Henry. He put out his big hand. No fist. The palm was outstretched. Henry seized it cordially.

"Well, I guess you whipped me, Hen," Mose said with a grin.

"I couldn't do it again," Hen replied. "I had a lot of help," he added as he thought of the little man who hit Mose on the back of the head with a monkey wrench. "You jest had some unlucky bounces, Mose."

A sigh of relief went up from the crowd. The men from the *White Ghost* and the *Old Maid* nodded with approval. Once again they started to talk—of work, of fun, of fires. And once again, the Bowery was the same old happy place.

In the daytime, men went about their business. The agreeable noises of the city filled the air. The gas lights were bright at night. The world was a pleasant place. There were fires. There were fights, with the Five Points gangs.

Mose was there all the time, but somehow he seemed different. Seemed like he was thinking of something else. He went to the new play at the Bowery Theatre with the rest of the Bowery B'hoys, and he went up to the Vauxhall Garden near Astor Place to hear the new orchestra. He went on the outing on the new railroad to Harlem. But his mind seemed to be somewhere else.

The *White Ghost* was given a new coat of white and gold. They shined her brass. Mose and the rest of the company cleaned and mended their uniforms. They ran to fires. The jeers and the jokes faded away. The old shine and pride and fighting spirit soon returned.

Sykesey noticed the change in his big friend. One

night they were walking home. It was quiet. Suddenly Sykesey turned to his companion. "I s'pose you'll tell me it's none of me business, an' prob'ly it ain't, but somethin's the matter with you, Mose."

"No. Nothin's the matter."

"But— Oh, well—" He couldn't press himself to pry into Mose's private affairs.

There was a long pause as they walked slowly, their steps echoing in the quiet of Mulberry Street. Then Mose said: "Yes, there is somethin'. I ain't told nobody yet. Didn't quite know how. But I guess I might as well. I'm goin' away."

"Away?"

"Yes. An' far away too."

Mose had never said a word about leaving New York. The idea of such a thing was too much for Sykesey. Without a second thought, he blurted out the questions that surged up. "When? Why? Where?" he fairly shouted.

Mose accepted his companion's excited demands calmly. "I didn't want to say anything about it until after everything was settled," he said.

Sykesey's surprise was so great that no more questions were asked. He could only gulp. Words wouldn't come. Mose continued. "The King of the

Sandwich Islands wrote to me an' asked me if I wouldn't come out there an' be the Chief of the Fire Department."

"Chief of the Sandwich Islands Fire Department!" Sykesey exploded.

"Yes." Mose grinned as he looked at Sykesey. "I didn't much want to go because I thought the biggest fires would be right here in the big city. So I thought I'd better stay right here an' fight 'em. But then, I got to readin' up. They got real big fires out there. Volcanoes, they are. They are big mountains, an' they are burnin' an' explodin' all the time. The big ones have names even. Mauna Loa, an' Kilauea, an'—oh, there's lots more of 'em."

"But Mose," Sykesey exclaimed, "what are we goin' to do about fires right here in New York?"

"There is lots of good firemen here. There will always be. But out there, maybe I kin do more good. Anyways the fires is bigger. Maybe they're so big I won't ever be able to put 'em out. But I can try to put 'em out, anyways." His look was determined.

"Yes, sir!" he exclaimed. "That's what I'm goin' to do. I'm goin' to be the Chief of the Sandwich Islands Fire Department!"

Mose quietly made his plans and said his goodbyes. At last the day came. Mose was at the Battery. He looked anxiously at his watch. Then his glance fell on his waiting ship.

The Captain said: "Come aboard. We got to sail."

Mose slowly turned toward the gangplank. His face was sad. "I can't understand it," he mused. "I thought Sykesey would be here. At least me old pal Sykesey. An' maybe even some of the others—"

He looked back at the city where he was born and reared. At the city he had so many times fought for, and saved from fire. "Not even Sykesey." A lump caught in his throat.

Then he heard a noise. A sound. From the east. Another from the north. It was music. Then there was more music. Bands of music! Was it a parade? What parade? He hadn't heard of a parade. But that is what it was.

He looked across the park. He saw the shine of brass. He caught the sight of red uniforms. White belts. Patent-leather hats and shoes. It was coming down Water Street.

He looked up Greenwich Street. Another band of music. A big one!

He looked up Broadway. What was this? Another band? It couldn't be! Who ever heard of three parades at once? But it was! Blue uniforms. Yellow belts. Red hats. Silver trumpets!

Three bands of music coming together. Turning into Battery Park. Three more behind them! Then three more!

The bands marched, and came together. They parted. And then— A sight for sad eyes! There was *Lady Washington Engine No. 40*!!

And there was Sykesey. And Jim Jeroloman, with his big gold earrings. And Orange County. And all the others!

Color, music, men, and machines flooded out of the streets and poured into the Park. Fire Engines. Hose Companies. Hook-and-Ladder Companies. Bands of Music!

The whole Volunteer Fire Department was there. Every man. Every single man!

The Mayor, with a red ribbon across his big white vest, and all the Common Council. They were there!

Women were there too. Lots of women, and children. He saw Linda, the beautiful segar girl. And Liza. Liza, his special gallus gal!

The *Old Maid*, with Big Henry in the lead. And the other engines. *Americus. Big Six. Eagle. Empire.*

Columbus. Honey Bee. Phoenix. Neptune. Red Rover. Old Turk. All of the engines!

The men broke ranks. They gathered around him. They shook his hands. They slapped his back. There were smiles and cheers and tears.

"We got to go," said the Captain.

They hoisted Mose to their shoulders and carried him on board the waiting ship.

"Up with the gangplank," shouted the Captain. "Hoist the mainsail!"

Ropes sang through their pulleys. Chains rattled. Men shouted. Wind filled the sails and the ship pulled away.

The volunteers lined their machines along the Upper Bay, at the tip of Manhattan's great heart. And in the center, the very center, was a small, white and gold machine, *Lady Washington Engine No. 40!*

All of the engine companies dropped their hoses into the water. Countless streams sprang up in the air from glistening brass nozzles. Countless cascades fell back. Countless rainbows, symbols of hope, shone in Manhattan's sunshine.

The ship sped away toward the Lower Bay and

the endless space of the ocean and the oceans beyond. Mose stood in the stern as the city, his city, faded from view. And the rainbows, and the sight of his old friends, and his beautiful, beloved engine, filled his eyes. The music of the bands, the cheers of men, and the thump of pumps and the crash of brakes filled his ears. And a big, deep affection for the volunteer firemen filled his heart.

A NOTE ON THE

Type

IN WHICH THIS BOOK WAS SET

❦ THE TEXT of this book is set in Caledonia, a Linotype face designed by W. A. Dwiggins. This type belongs to the family of printing types called "modern face" by printers—a term used to mark the change in style of type-letters that occurred about 1800. Caledonia borders on the general design of Scotch Modern, but is more freely drawn than that letter.

❦ THIS BOOK was composed, printed, and bound by H. Wolff, New York. Paper manufactured by P. H. Glatfelter Co., Spring Grove, Pa. Designed by Charles Farrell.

999   F.W.